Thank you...

... for purchasing this copy of Reading for Literacy for ages 9-10. We hope that you find our worksheets, teachers' notes and display materials helpful as part of your programme of literacy activities.

Please note that photocopies can only be made for use by the purchasing institution. Supplying copies to other schools, institutions or individuals breaches the copyright licence. Thank you for your help in this.

This Reading for Literacy book is part of our growing range of educational titles. Most of our books are individual workbooks but, due to popular demand, we are now introducing a greater number of photocopiable titles especially for teachers. You may like to look out for:

READING FOR LITERACY for Reception
and for ages 5-7, 7-8, 8-9, 9-10, 10-11

WRITING FOR LITERACY for ages 5-7, 7-8, 8-9, 9-10, 10-11

SPELLING FOR LITERACY for ages 5-7, 7-8, 8-9, 9-10, 10-11

NUMERACY TODAY for ages 5-7, 7-9, 9-11

HOMEWORK TODAY for ages 7-8, 8-9, 9-10, 10-11

BEST HANDWRITING for ages 7-11

To find details of our other publications, please visit our website: **www.acblack.com**

ABOUT THIS BOOK

As with all our photocopiable resource books we have kept the teachers' notes to a minimum as we are well aware that teachers will use their own professionalism in using our materials.

At the start of each Unit we list some of the National Literacy Strategy Objectives that the Unit may cover. We are grateful to the Department for Education and Skills for their permission to quote the Objectives.

Some of the Units are linked to others as indicated by their titles.

Many Units feature reading activities that can be undertaken individually or in a small group situation, alongside the teacher or support assistant.

Some Units could be copied onto Overhead Projector Transparencies for use with a large group or the whole class.

The Units vary in their level of difficulty and teachers will match Units to the ability levels of the pupils in their classes.

Most Units are four pages long. All of them provide worthwhile activities as well as useful practice for tests.

Extracts from the National Literacy Strategy Framework for Teaching, © Crown copyright 1998, reproduced by kind permission of the Department for Education and Skills.

Contents ...

Year 5

Term 1

Contents ...

Year 5

Term 2

Contents ...
Year 5

Term 3

The objective indicated on the contents pages, is the main focus for each Unit. Each Unit can, however, be used for many different objectives and further suggestions of objectives are found at the start of each Unit.

This unit addresses the Literacy Strategy:
Term 1 objective   1: to analyse the features of a good opening and compare a number of story openings.
Term 1 objective 11: to experiment with alternative ways of opening a story using, e.g. description, action or dialogue.

YEAR	UNIT	Sheet
5	**1**	**A**

Name   **Story Openings**

Read these three passages. They are the openings of three different stories.

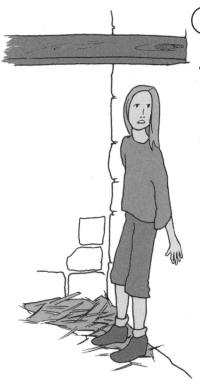

① Jane stood frozen with fear in the corner of the old barn. She listened so hard her head hurt. A fly was buzzing its way out of a spider's web and the hot breeze hummed through the cracks in the stones. The palms of her hands were pressed flat against the cold stone wall behind her; they were damp with sweat. She felt as though the rest of the population had moved to another planet. Terror consumed her.

②

My sister giggled as I came through into the dining room.

"Shut up!" I said.

"You look very smart, dear," said Gran. "He'll break a few girls' hearts, won't he Sally?"

Why does everyone make you feel embarrassed just because you dress up smartly for a change? I was only going to the cinema. It was no big deal.

"Is <u>she</u> going?" asked my sister Kate loudly, so everyone else would hear her.

I ignored her.

"Is she?" she said again.

"Who's 'she'?" said Mum.

"I haven't got the foggiest idea," I said, looking at the floor.

"Yes you have. He has, Mum. Her name's Laura and she's in his class."

③

My family are a complete embarrassment to me. Dad works at Hackers Building Supplies and Mum's a nurse. There's nothing wrong with that, but they think they're in the fifties. They weren't even alive until the end of the sixties! They listen to the Everly Brothers and Elvis all the time. They think they're cool and try to get on with my friends; they abbreviate their names – "Hi Kev," or "Hi Jim." No one calls James that.

Can you imagine parents' evening when Mum and Dad turn up in leather gear, complete with studs and fringes? The Harley-Davidson parked next to James' Dad's BMW in the car park! When Miss Baker sees them she looks them up and down a few times before she can speak. I can imagine what she says in the staff room.

Anyway, people get the wrong impression and three weeks ago real trouble began. There was a knock on the door while we were having tea. Dad opened it.
.

"We're looking for a Mr Steven Beran," said the taller of the two policeman standing framed in the doorway.

"Yes, that's me, how can I help?" said Dad cheerily.

"We have reason to believe you have stolen materials worth £2,000 from Hackers Building Supplies."

Write the answers to these questions.

1. Create a title for each of the three stories. The title should give the reader a hint about the story to follow.

    Story 1 _____

    Story 2 _____

    Story 3 _____

2. Which one of the three openings most makes you want to read the rest of the story? Give two reasons for your answer.

    Favourite Opening _____

    Reasons _____

    _____

    _____

    _____

    _____

    _____

    _____

3. Which of the three openings do you think the least interesting? Give reasons why you may not choose to read the rest of the story.

    Least Favourite Opening _____

    Reasons _____

    _____

    _____

    _____

    _____

4. Look at the opening of your reading book and other books you know. Think about what makes them successful in gaining the reader's interest.
    Write your own opening to a story. Try to make your reader want to find out what happened next. You could use description, action or dialogue.
    Write in the space below or on a separate piece of paper.

YEAR **5** | UNIT **2** | Sheet **A**   *Name*   Tabitha's Sorrow

Tabitha's Sorrow

I glared with loathing at the leather jacket opposite me. It wasn't the jacket that I objected to. It was the oily, glistening face that it belonged to. This was Keith, Mum's boyfriend. He was the most disgusting creature that I had ever had the misfortune to meet. I couldn't imagine what my Mum saw in him. He obviously thought that the studded, leather jacket made him appear cool and young-looking. He had no idea how sad he looked. I mean he was nearly forty, he had crooked teeth and his hair was getting thin on the top. He looked nothing like my Dad used to look.

"So what sort of motor bike have you got then?"

"Well, actually, I don't have a bike," he stammered.

I snorted in disgust, to make sure that he got the message that I thought he was a total waste of space.

"So why are you wearing that jacket then, if you haven't got a bike? That's a biker's jacket, or didn't you know?" I stared at his crooked teeth, to make sure he knew that I had noticed them.

"I'm not very good with anything mechanical, actually. I guess I just like the jacket, Tabitha" came the pathetic reply. "Don't you like it? Perhaps you might like to try it on?"

"Nah, it's not my kind of thing."

I was pleased to see that he looked a bit disappointed when I said that. I reckon he had been trying to impress me by turning up in that jacket. He knew I loved motor bikes, but I left him in no doubt that I was seriously not impressed.

Mum drifted into the room looking as young and lovely as ever. Since Dad had died two years ago, Mum and me had been fine together. We'd had our ups and downs but we'd had some really great times as well. We used to love going down the shopping centre, on a Saturday afternoon, trying on different dresses, and giggling at ourselves in the changing rooms. That was before Keith came on the scene. Now Mum goes off with him on a Saturday afternoon to watch him play football. He plays for some club, for ancient doddery blokes who think they can still play football. Mum says that she likes watching him play, and that the fresh air does her good.

"Why don't you come with us this week, Tabitha? You might enjoy it." Mum's voice was always gentle and reasonable, and I knew that she was only trying to make me feel wanted, but I was in no mood for 'reasonable'. Reasonable was me and Mum, not me, Mum, and Keith.

"I want to go shopping, Mum, like we used to. Come on Mum, let's go down the Arndale Centre, and try on some tops like we used to. It'll be fun, just the two of us." I stared straight at Keith to make sure he got the message that he definitely wasn't included.

"No Tabitha, I'm going to the football with Keith, you know that."

"I'm sick of him. Why is he always hanging round here? What does he want? We don't need him. We're all right on our own, aren't we Mum?"

Mum didn't answer, but just looked at me with those dark sorrowful eyes, that I had seen so many times over the last two years. She just put on her blue and white scarf, tucked the wisps of blond hair into her bobble hat, took Keith by the arm and left.

Don't I matter anymore, Mum? Tears sprung from my eyes as I flung myself across Mum's bed. Aren't I important anymore? Dad would have been there to cheer me up and make me laugh. The longing inside me to see my Dad pressed me down into the mattress. The pain filled my head. The hurt deep in my stomach was still just as real as it had been two years ago, when the Police had come to tell Mum and me about the accident. I can remember thinking that Dad couldn't die. That it was a dream. But over the terrible months that followed, I had realised that it was no dream. Mum and I clung to each other, looking out for each other, cheering the other one up when they looked sad. Slowly, over time, life had got back to... well, not normal; it would never be normal again.

I lay on my bed, and put my mind to remembering all the happy days that the three of us had had together. When I thought of my Dad, it was as if I could really see his face, feel his hands, smell his breath. I remembered all the details, all the sounds, even the exact words my Dad had said.

"Now Tabby." (My name was Tabitha but Dad had called me Tabby since I was a baby. To be honest I had stopped liking it years ago, but I never told him.) "Give us one of your songs." He liked hearing me sing, and was always asking me to sing the current chart topper. As I lay there thinking about Dad, I became even more determined to work out a plan to get rid of Keith. Somehow I had to get Mum to see what a loser he was.

Dad had always been brilliant at mending things round the house, when they broke or went wrong. Mum and me had been at a total loss to know what to do after he died when the heating packed up and water was squirting out from one of the pipes. It had cost us a fortune getting the plumber out on a Sunday morning.

What if something 'accidentally' went wrong when Keith was here, and Mum asked him to sort it out? He had already said how hopeless he was with his hands. He would have no idea what to do. Mum would

see how useless he was... I set my mind to planning the little 'accident'.

Dialogue (speech) can tell you what a character is like, both by <u>what</u> they say, and <u>how</u> they say it.

1. How do you think Tabitha is feeling when she says, "So why are you wearing that jacket then, if you haven't got a bike? That's a biker's jacket, or didn't you know?"

   _____

   _____

   _____

2. Look through the text, and underline/highlight the different words that the writer has used, after someone has spoken, to show <u>how</u> they have spoken.

   1 _____

   2 _____

   3 _____

3. The words 'she said' or 'he said' after a character has spoken are not always the best words to use. Think of five other verbs that you could use to make a story more interesting. The first one is an example from the text.

   1 __**he stammered**_____   **4** _____

   2 _____   **5** _____

   3 _____   **6** _____

4. Sort the six words that you wrote in question 3, by putting them in the boxes below. Decide which category you think they fit, to show different characteristics and emotions.

angry	**upset**	**happy**
quiet	**careful**	**other category**

5. Now think of some more words that could replace 'said' and write them in the correct box.

6. Which phrases in the text tell you that Tabitha is really very unhappy?

    ☐ **I became even more determined to get rid of Keith.**

    ☐ **Don't I matter anymore, Mum?**

    ☐ **That was before Keith was on the scene.**

    ☐ **He had no idea how sad he looked.**

    ☐ **I was in no mood for 'reasonable'.**

    ☐ **The hurt deep in my stomach...**

7. How do you think Tabitha felt about Keith? Explain as fully as you can.

    _____

    _____

    _____

    _____

8. What do you learn about Dad from Tabitha's description?

    _____

    _____

    _____

9. Why do you think Mum did not answer Tabitha when she said, "We're all right on our own, aren't we Mum?"

    _____

    _____

    _____

10. Why did Tabitha want to plan a 'little accident'?

    _____

    _____

    _____

11. From whose point of view is the story written?

    _____

12. What do you think Tabitha will do to try and get rid of Keith? Write the next part of the story. If you want to, you could write it from Mum or Keith's point of view.

YEAR	UNIT	Sheet
5	3	A

Name   Becoming a Reader

On these two pages you will find a piece of writing based on the author's own experiences. It shows how a person can grow to love reading different types of texts. Perhaps it will make you think about the things that have influenced your reading.

Becoming a Reader

It wasn't until Jude was an adult with children of her own that she wondered how she had become a reader. She wasn't concerned with how she learnt to read (though she did have some distant memories of doing just that) but how she had become a lover of books. Was it just because the bus stop where she caught the bus home each day after school happened to be outside the doors of the library? It was, after all, much more enjoyable to be in the warmth of that building choosing a book to read, than it was to be waiting in the queue for a bus, particularly in the cold days of winter.

The library must have helped, as it gave her access to such a huge range of books. As an adult she remembered, with a fondness, the smell of the polished library floors, the quiet calm inside, the mystery that was the adult section (a place as yet out of bounds to her) and of course the hours spent browsing in books until she found one that she knew she simply must borrow to read. Despite all this she didn't feel that her frequent visits to the library were the main reason for her love of books.

Far more important she felt, was the large old wooden bookcase in her childhood home. From a very early age, the books with their old-fashioned plain covers, held an enduring fascination. She marvelled that, as young people, her parents should have had only books that looked outwardly so uninviting, had such small print, so very few illustrations, a lack of colour and such thin flimsy pages. Perhaps it was the very fact that the cover gave no clues as to what was held on the pages that indeed made the books more enticing, for she loved to delve into these uninterestingly disguised books to discover what adventures and mysteries were inside.

Amongst the range of books, both fiction and non-fiction, were two that became particular favourites. One was a small and rather insignificant looking anthology of poetry, wrapped in a black cover and entitled 'The Dragon Book of Verse', and the other was a novel called 'The Lamplighter'.

The first thing that attracted her as a child to 'The Dragon Book of Verse' was its title.

Anything mentioning dragons must surely be exciting. She began to regularly dip into this volume, and found many pieces of treasure in the form of poems. Some were not easy to understand at first, but somehow were made easier to comprehend by reading them aloud, feeling what the words might mean and enjoying the rhythm of the language.

The works in this book included poems by such well known poets as William Shakespeare, John Keats, Christina Rossetti and Lewis Carroll, as well as many others with names that she had never heard of before. There was a new admiration born in her on discovering that some of these poems were known by heart by her mother.   A woman who did all the ordinary things in life that other mothers did too, had all these wonderful pieces of language locked away in her head. This made Jude read the poetry more carefully and she soon found she too had some of them stored permanently away in her mind, and could recall them at will.

In contrast 'The Lamplighter' was a novel, which she knew to be old by the language in it and by its presentation in an old plain cover. This book, however, was somewhat different from all the other old pieces of fiction in the bookcase: the pages were edged in gold, the cover was slightly padded and the few full page black and white illustrations were immediately followed by a page of tissue. She presumed that this served to protect the pictures, though she couldn't see why they should need protection. The features that defined this book from all the others made it seem special, hence more tempting to read. The story also (as she discovered on first opening the book) had an alternative title of 'An Orphan Girl's Struggles and Triumphs'. She felt that having a choice of two titles also gave the book an air of importance, and whilst she preferred the main title of the book, the extra one gave a much clearer indication of the content of the story. Many happy hours of childhood were spent reading and rereading that particular tale.

Whilst the two books detailed were particularly treasured by the young Jude, there were of course many others she enjoyed. Amongst the other books in the old bookcase were novels by Charles Dickens and Edgar Allen Poe, books about the locality in which she lived, poems by Robert Louis Stevenson and many factual books.

As an adult her memories of these were, she was quite sure, a major influence in making her a lover of books and literature. Of course all the more modern books of her childhood, the brightly covered and illustrated annuals and tales of adventure written for junior readers, also played their part as did the many other reading experiences she had long since forgotten. The most important thing was, after all, that however she got there, she was most undoubtedly a lover of the written word.

Name _____   Becoming a Reader

📖 Write the adjective used to describe the library floor. _____

📖 Which part of the library was Jude not allowed into? _____

📖 What was the old bookcase made of? _____

📖 What type of book was 'The Dragon Book of Verse'? _____

📖 What first attracted Jude to this book and why?

_____

_____

_____

📖 What was Jude surprised to discover her mother could do?

_____

_____

Can you do this?

📖 What was the title of the novel referred to in the text?

_____

📖 It also had an alternative title. Write it below.

_____

_____

📖 Name two authors whose novels were also found in the old bookcase.

_____

_____

📖 **On the back.**
Write about your favourite book and what first made you want to read it.
Discuss your work with a friend.

📖 From the information preceding the text, what would you think is the first name of the writer? _____

📖 Name four of the poets whose poems could be found in 'The Dragon Book of Verse'.

_____

_____

_____

_____

📖 In the text, what are described as 'pieces of treasure'? _____

📖 What type of book was 'The Lamplighter'? _____

📖 What made 'The Lamplighter' appear more special than many of the other old books? _____

_____

_____

📖 What was useful about 'The Lamplighter's' other title?

_____

_____

📖 What is the word used in the text, that means the same as 'understand'? _____

📖 What is the name given to a book which is published every year? _____

📖 Write about your own reading experiences. Can you remember the name of your favourite book from when you were little? What type of books do you like to read now? Which is your favourite of all the books you have ever read?

_____

_____

_____

_____

_____

_____

_____

This unit addresses the Literacy Strategy:
Term 1 objective   5: to understand dramatic conventions including: the conventions of scripting (e.g. stage directions, asides); how character
can be communicated in words and gesture; how tension can be built up through pace, silences and delivery.

Ellie and Jonah

TWO CHILDREN CROUCH IN THE SEMI-DARKNESS BEHIND A DUSTBIN IN AN ALLEYWAY.

ELLIE: What's that?

JONAH: I don't know but it's getting nearer.

(A FAINT METALLIC RHYTHMIC SOUND CAN BE HEARD OFF-STAGE.)

ELLIE: It's coming this way. Let's run!

JONAH: No, we're safe here. They won't think to look down the alley, and besides,
I'm here so you don't need to worry. (TO HIMSELF.) Thank goodness she
doesn't know how scared I am.

(THEY LISTEN, SILENTLY, FOR A FEW MINUTES.)

ELLIE: It's stopped now. I think we can go. Put your torch on.

(ELLIE STANDS UP FROM BEHIND THE DUSTBIN.)

JONAH: No, not yet. (JONAH PULLS ELLIE BACK DOWN.) It's not safe.

(SILENCE EXCEPT FOR ELLIE AND JONAH BREATHING HEAVILY. THE NOISE STARTS AGAIN BUT LOUDER.)

ELLIE: They're coming, Jonah. They're coming. (ELLIE STARTS TO CRY.)
I want Mum.

JONAH: Sssh, we must be very quiet and still, Ellie.
It's all right. We'll be fine. Hold tight on
to me. Snuggle under my coat.

(JONAH STROKES ELLIE'S LONG, LANK HAIR.)

ELLIE: But, but they're going to find us, and take
us away, and ...

JONAH: No, I won't let them. I'll fight them. You'll
see. It'll all be all right. I'll look after you
until we find Mum.

(NOISE STARTS AGAIN - VERY LOUD. JONAH COVERS ELLIE'S MOUTH WITH HIS HAND. VOICES CAN BE
HEARD OFF-STAGE.)

VOICES: I'm sure I saw them running this way. The little scum went down the alley.

JONAH: Huh! (SHARP INTAKE OF BREATH.)

ELLIE: (ELLIE MAKES STIFLED WHIMPERS, AND STARES OFF-STAGE IN THE DIRECTION OF THE
VOICES.)

VOICES: No, they headed off down in the direction of the river. Go down Briggs
Road. We'll cut them off.

(TAPPING NOISE FADES AWAY SLOWLY.)

JONAH: They're going. It's going to be OK. We're safe, and look Ellie it's getting light now. We'll wait here for a minute just to make sure and then we'll double back to the church. Father Pat will help us, I know he will. (PAUSE) I've still got some biscuits. Do you want one Ellie?

ELLIE: Ooh, yes please. I'm starving, but you said they were all gone.

JONAH: I was just pretending. I thought we might need them later.

(JONAH UNWRAPS THE BISCUITS AND GIVES ONE TO ELLIE. THEY MUNCH THEIR BISCUITS TOGETHER.)

JONAH: OK, I think it's all clear now. Let's go.

(THEY CREEP CAUTIOUSLY OUT FROM BEHIND THE BIN AND STRETCH THEIR ACHING LIMBS.)

ELLIE: My legs hurt from being squidged up all that time.

JONAH: Never mind Shortie, a quick walk will soon sort that out.

ELLIE: Don't call me Shortie, I hate it and anyway…

(SUDDENLY THE NOISE STARTS AGAIN, EXTREMELY LOUD AND CLOSE.)

JONAH: Ellie, quick, hold my hand. RUN!

(JONAH GRABS ELLIE'S HAND AND DRAGS HER OFF-STAGE AWAY FROM THE DIRECTION OF THE NOISE.)

Read the playscript carefully then answer the questions.

1. Where is the play set?

    _____

2. How old do you think Jonah is?   [ ]

3. How old do you think Ellie is?   [ ]

4. What clues from the script help you to judge their ages?

    Jonah_____

    _____

    _____

    _____

    Ellie _____

    _____

    _____

    _____

5.   Think of two adjectives that describe Jonah's character.

6.   Copy the part from the script that makes you think he is like that.

_____

_____

_____

7.   Write some statements about how you think Ellie is feeling.

_____

_____

_____

8.   Who do you think Jonah and Ellie might be hiding from?

_____

_____

9.   Look in a dictionary and write the meanings of these words.

stifled _____

_____

lank _____

_____

whimper _____

_____

10.   Choose the correct endings for these sentences from the boxes below.
     In the Ellie and Jonah playscript:

Each new speaker...   _____

Each speaker's name...   _____

Stage directions...   _____

Brackets can also show...   _____

(**is written in capitals.**)   (**are written in brackets.**)

(**has a new line.**)   (**sound effects.**)

11.   Write a list of props (objects and furniture) you might need for this play.

_____   _____

_____   _____

_____   _____

12.   What sort of lighting would you have for this scene? How would it change when the people making the noise first go away?

_____

_____

_____

13.   How do the sound effects build up the tension?

_____

_____

_____

14.   An **aside** is when a character talks to himself or the audience and other characters are not meant to hear. Find an example of an aside in the play and copy it out.

_____

_____

15.   A stage direction tells the actor how to speak or what to do.
Find three examples of stage directions.

   1. _____

   2. _____

   3. _____

16.   Sometimes there are silences or pauses on the stage. What is the purpose of these silences?

_____

_____

17.   A scene in a play is like a chapter in a book. Each scene can be set in a different place or time. Think about what you think might have happened to Jonah and Ellie in the play before this scene takes place. What has happened to their Mum? Why are they being chased?
With a partner, write the scene which comes before this one. Remember to start a new line for each new speaker and set it out like the scene you have just read. Put in the stage directions and the sound effects.

This unit addresses the Literacy Strategy:
Term 1 objective   3: to investigate how characters are presented, referring to the text; through dialogue, action and description; how the reader
                        responds to them (as victims, heroes etc.); through examining their relationships with other characters.
Term 1 objective   8: to investigate and collect different examples of word play, relating form to meaning.

YEAR 5	UNIT 5	Sheet A

Name   **Word Play**

WORD PLAY

"My pen's run out!" shouted my sister.
"Go and fetch it then," I said.

"The computer's gone down," said Dad.
"Down where?" I enquired.

"The car's up the creek," moaned Mum,
"Which creek's that?" I asked.

"You're for the high jump!" they all yelled.
So I closed my mouth tightly,
and didn't say a word.

1.   Do you think that this piece of writing is in the form of poetry or prose?
      Try to explain your answer.

      _____

      _____

2.   Do you think the narrator is a boy or a girl? Try to explain your answer.

      _____

      _____

3a.   What did the sister mean by her exclamation?

      _____

b.   How did the narrator interpret her statement?

      _____

4a.   What did the dad mean?

      _____

b.   How was this interpreted?

      _____

Name _____   Word Play

5a.   What did the mum mean?

_____

b.   How was this interpreted?

_____

Each of these pictures shows an example of a 'play on words'. Try to identify the familiar expression that each picture represents.

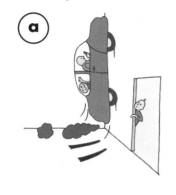

1.   He's certainly got his head screwed on. ☐

2.   She was over the moon when she heard the news. ☐

3.   "That boy is driving me up the wall," said the teacher. ☐

4.   He was so pleased, he looked like the cat that got the cream. ☐

5.   "I'll give you a hand," said the girl helpfully. ☐

6.   He was so happy, he was like a dog with two tails. ☐

7.   Which three expressions are to do with being really pleased about something? ☐ ☐ ☐

Word Play

Read the following sentences. They all include expressions that we hear regularly but that are not literally correct or true. With a friend discuss what each one means. Choose one of the expressions to illustrate, then see if your friend can identify which one you chose and what it means.

(**a**) The next programme is a fly-on-the-wall documentary.

(**b**) I was up the creek without a paddle.

(**c**) She ran the race as though she had two left feet.

(**d**) He got really angry so I told him to keep his hair on.

(**e**) It's a good idea not to bite off more than you can chew.

(**f**) She looks at the world through rose-tinted spectacles.

(**g**) It's no use crying over spilt milk.

PROVERBS

Proverbs are old sayings or expressions. People use them to give simple pieces of advice or to express an opinion.

(**a**) The grass is greener on the other side.

(**b**) Look before you leap.

(**c**) A stitch in time saves nine.

(**d**) Many hands make light work.

(**e**) The early bird catches the worm.

(**f**) Too many cooks spoil the broth.

(**g**) Don't count your chickens before they hatch.

(**h**) Make hay while the sun shines.

The early bird catches the worm.

1a. Which two of the proverbs could mean the opposite of each other?

b. Why are they opposites? _____

_____

_____

2a. Which three proverbs could mean more-or-less the same thing?

b. What do they all mean? _____

_____

_____

3. Choose a proverb. Prepare a short explanation of its meaning to present to your class. Can the class identify the one you are describing?

_____

_____

_____

_____

This unit addresses the Literacy Strategy:
Term 1 objective   11: to experiment with alternative ways of opening a story using e.g. description, action, or dialogue.
Term 3 objective   2: to identify the point of view from which a story is told and how this affects the reader's response.
Term 3 objective   3: to change point of view, e.g. tell incidents or describe a situation from the point of view of another character or perspective.

YEAR	UNIT	Sheet
5	6	A

Name

Lost Dog

Below are several different ways of beginning a story about a lost dog. Each of them is a possible way of starting the same story, even though different titles are used.

Winston's Great Adventure

Winston was a large, clumsy and, some would say, rather dozy Old English Sheepdog. He had a good appetite, often rather too good for the liking of the family he lived with. In addition to enjoying his own food, he liked nothing better than to discover other foods that were not actually for him. Since his birth, three years before, he had often been in trouble for sampling tasty morsels that were not destined to become dog food. These incidents included the time he ate Santa's mince pie on Christmas Eve (though he left the bearded old gent his sherry), the occasion when he discovered he could open the fridge (a lock had to be fitted later) and of course the memorable event when a large box of chocolates was

left unguarded for a moment and disappeared, complete with wrappers.

It was this uncanny ability to track down food that led to what he liked to think of as his great adventure, and what the family always referred to as the dreadful day they lost the dog.

The Vanishing Dog

It was a chilly morning in early November. One of those autumn days that looked like summer, but felt distinctly like winter. The Benson family got up at seven, just as they did every weekday. Little did they know that this day would be far from ordinary.

Billy, the elder of the two Benson children, went downstairs first and, as usual, expected Winston, the large lovable family dog, to greet him. Winston was always eager to greet the first family member to appear each morning as he was always anxious for his breakfast. This morning however there was an unusual quietness in the hall. Billy suddenly realised that the dog was nowhere to be seen. He quickly glanced round the kitchen. There was an empty dog bed, and no sign of furry footsteps anywhere. Winston had mysteriously vanished.

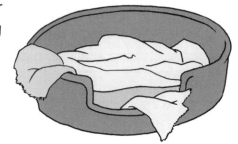

Where is Winston?

"Where is Winston?" Billy Benson shouted urgently up the stairs in the direction of his parents' room.

"What are you shouting about?" said Dad, appearing at the top of the stairs. "He's down there of course."

"If he was down here I wouldn't be shouting," replied Billy in an anxious voice.

"What's happening?" came the sleepy tones of Ellis, his younger sister.

"It's Winston, he's disappeared!"

Dad and Ellis, joined a few seconds later by Mum, were soon downstairs with Billy hunting for the dog.

"Well he doesn't seem to be in the house, yet I cannot imagine how he can possibly have got out," concluded Dad when they had searched everywhere they could think of.

"I had better ring the police and report him missing," said Mum, sounding very worried.

Ellis began to cry.

My Great Adventure.

I am Winston, a rather handsome and athletic Old English Sheepdog. I live with the Benson Family, where my role is to be their fearless protector. One day, a few weeks ago, I had rather a marvellous adventure, though unfortunately my family saw very little of it. Somehow they must have found out what a daring dog I had been, unafraid of risks and able to find my way across streets and fields, as they made a great fuss of me when I was returned to them. I'm sure I could have easily found my way home again but the policeman I met in the butcher's shop was kind enough to escort me. I must admit I would rather he had let me finish the sausages I was enjoying first. Still his heart was in the right place I suppose.

Now I have introduced myself I will tell you about my adventurous day, a day that tested my courage, resourcefulness and speed. It began when I woke up as usual, and began to look forward to my breakfast.

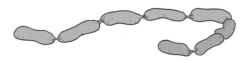

Name _____   Lost Dog

1. How many different ways are shown to begin the same story? _____

2. Which title do you think is best? Give reasons for your answer.

    _____

    _____

    _____

3. Name the five main characters.

    _____   _____   _____

    _____   _____

4. Write the title of the only story opening that names all five characters.

    _____

5. Write the title of the story opening that is written in the 'first person', by the dog.

    _____

6. Which of the four versions opens with dialogue?

    _____

7. Which two of the openings tells you that the 'adventure' is completed within a day?

    _____

    _____

8. From the opening 'Where is Winston?', list below the
    words used instead of 'said'.

    _____

    _____

    _____

    _____

9. Which two of the story openings lead you to believe that it will be a light-hearted tale? Give reasons for your answer.

_____

_____

_____

_____

10. Which of the story openings, introduces the action in the middle of the story?

_____

11. Which opening do you think is the most effective? Explain your answer.

_____

_____

_____

_____

_____

12. In the opening of 'My Great Adventure' we are told that the family made a great fuss of Winston when he was returned to them. He believed that it was because they understood the events of the day. What was the most likely reason?

_____

_____

_____

_____

13. Invent a title and a story opening of your own for this story. If you have time, you may continue the story.

You could write it from the point of view of Billy or Ellis.

Decide whether your story will be humorous or serious.

YEAR	UNIT	Sheet
5	7	A

Name _____

Black Beauty

The author Anna Sewell, best known for her book 'Black Beauty', was born in Great Yarmouth (Norfolk) in March 1820. Her life was blighted by ill health and she died in May 1878. Anna Sewell hoped that her book would help people to be more caring towards their horses.

Remember - there were no cars then, so horses were the main means of transport.

The story of 'Black Beauty' is written as if being told by the horse himself.

One day, late in the autumn, my master had a long journey to go on business. I was put into the dog-cart, and John went with his master. I always liked to go in the dog-cart, it was so light, and the high wheels ran along so pleasantly. There had been a great deal of rain, and now the wind was very high and blew the dry leaves across the road in a shower. We went merrily along till we came to the toll-bar and the low wooden bridge. The river banks were rather high, and the bridge, instead of rising, went across just level, so that in the middle, if the river was full, the water would be nearly up to the woodwork and planks; but as there were good substantial rails on each side, people did not mind it.

The man at the gate said the river was rising fast, and he feared it would be a bad night. Many of the meadows were under water, and in one low part of the road the water was half-way up to my knees; the bottom was good, and master drove gently, so it was no matter.

When we got to the town, of course I had a good bait; but as the master's business engaged him a long time, we did not start for home till rather late in the afternoon. The wind was then much higher, and I heard the master say to John he had never been out in such a storm; and so I thought, as we went along the skirts of a wood, where the great branches were swaying about like twigs, and the rushing sound of the wind through the trees was terrible.

"I wish we were well out of this wood," said my master.

"Yes, sir," said John, "it would be rather awkward if one of these branches came down upon us."

The words were scarcely out of his mouth, when there was a groan, a crack, and a splitting sound, and tearing, crashing down amongst the other trees, came an oak, torn up by the roots, which fell right across the road just before us. I will never say I was not frightened, for I was. I stopped still, and I believe I trembled. Of course I did not turn round or run away; I was not brought up to do that. John jumped out and in a moment was at my head.

"That was very near touch," said my master. "What's to be done now?"

"Well, sir, we can't drive over that tree nor yet get round it; there will be nothing for it but to go back to the four crossways, and that will be a good six miles before we get

round to the wooden bridge again. It will make us late, but the horse is fresh."
So back we went, and round by the crossroads; but by the time we got to the bridge, it
was very nearly dark, and we could just see that the water was over the middle of it;
but as that happened sometimes when the floods were out, master did not stop.
We were going along at a good pace, but the moment my feet touched the first part of
the bridge, I felt sure there was something wrong. I dare not go forward, and so I make
a dead stop. "Go on, Beauty," said my master, giving me a touch with the whip; but I
dare not stir. He gave me a sharp cut; I jumped, but I dared not go forward.
"There's something wrong, sir," said John; and he sprang out of the dog-cart and came
to my head and looked all about. He tried to lead me forward. "Come on, Beauty,
what's the matter?" Of course I could not tell him, but I knew very well that the bridge
was not safe.
Just then the man at the toll-gate on the other side ran out out the house, tossing a
torch about like one mad.
"Hoy, hoy, hoy, halloo, stop!" he cried.
"What's the matter?" shouted my master.
"The bridge is broken in the middle, and part of it is carried away; if you come on you'll
be into the river."
"Thank God!" said my master. "You Beauty!" said John; and taking the bridle, he
gently turned me round to the right-hand road by the river side. The sun had set some
time, the wind seemed to have lulled off after that furious blast which tore up the tree.
It grew darker and darker, and more and more still. I trotted quietly along, the wheels
hardly making a sound on the soft road.
For a good while neither master nor John spoke; and then the master began to speak in
a serious voice. I could not understand much of what they said, but I found they
thought that if I had gone on as the master wanted me, most likely the bridge would
have given way under us, and horse, chaise, master, and man would have fallen into the
river; and as the current was flowing very strongly, and there was no light and no help
at hand, it was more than likely we should all have been drowned. Master said, God
had given men reason by which they could find out things for themselves; but He had
given animals knowledge which did not depend on reason, much more prompt and
perfect in its way, by which they had often saved the lives of men.
John had stories to tell of dogs and horses, and the wonderful things they had done.
He thought people did not value their animals half enough, nor make friends of them as
they ought to. I am sure he makes friends of them if ever a man does.
At last we came to the park gates, and found the gardener looking out for us. He said
that mistress had been in a dreadful way ever since dark, fearing some accident had
happened; and that she had sent James off on Justice, the roan cob, towards the
wooden bridge to make enquiry after us.
We saw a light at the hall door and at the upper windows, and as we came up mistress
ran out saying, "Are you really safe, my dear? Oh! I have been so anxious, fancying all
sorts of things. Have you had no accident?"
"No, my dear; but if your Black Beauty had not been wiser then we were, we should all
have been carried down the river at the wooden bridge."
I heard no more, as they went into the house and John took me to the stable. Oh! what
a supper he gave me that night - a good bran mash and some crushed beans with my
oats, and such a thick bed of straw. I was glad of it, for I was tired.

Name _____   Black Beauty

📖 Who was the author of the novel 'Black Beauty'?

_____

📖 In which county was she born?

_____

📖 How old was she when she died?

_____

📖 What fell across the road just in front of Black Beauty?

_____

📖 How many extra miles did Black Beauty have to travel to the next bridge?

_____

📖 What was the name of the other horse mentioned in the text?

_____

📖 What did Black Beauty know before the men?

_____

_____

_____

📖 What would have been the likely outcome if Black Beauty had stepped onto the bridge?

_____

_____

_____

_____

📖 How was Black Beauty rewarded for saving the men?

_____

_____

_____

📖 On the back - Illustrate a scene from the text.

Name   **Black Beauty**

On the lines below write a paragraph summarizing the content of the text.

_____

_____

_____

_____

_____

_____

_____

_____

Describe the weather on the first part of the journey home.

_____

_____

From reading the text what do you think a 'dog-cart' is?

_____

_____

What do you think is meant by 'the skirts of the wood'?

_____

_____

In the text it says '...He had given animals knowledge which did not depend on reason...'. What is meant by this?

_____

_____

_____

_____

Who was waiting at the park gates, and why?

_____

_____

On the back - write the story from the point of view of 'The Master'.

| YEAR 5 | UNIT 8 | Sheet A |

Name   The Lynmouth Lifeboat

In 1899, the Lynmouth lifeboat made a dramatic journey to rescue the crew of the boat known as The Forest Hall. The Forest Hall had been caught in a force 8 gale on the afternoon of January 12th. She was trapped in Porlock Bay, in Somerset, and sending out distress signals.

The morning of the 12th January was very stormy. Clouds were scudding across the skies and thousands of white waves were crashing on the beach. Coxswain, Jack Crowcombe, the leader of the twelve-oar Lynmouth lifeboat, reckoned that they would be called on soon. When the call came, his first reaction was to check the launching ramp. He was dismayed to see that it was unapproachable due to the heavy seas. Jack weighed up all the possibilities, and finally came to the conclusion that they must launch the lifeboat from Porlock. The crew protested that this was madness, as Porlock was 15 land miles away, over very difficult roads. After some discussion, however, it was decided that this was the only possible way to launch the lifeboat.

First, the men gathered together all the equipment they would need, and mounted the boat on its carriage. Once this was done, they harnessed the coach horses, and set off pushing, pulling and shoving. The first obstacle was Countisbury Hill, a long steep climb. As they soldiered on up the hill, disaster struck, when half way up, a wheel came off the lifeboat carriage. Even though a gale was blowing, and the wind was lashing, they made a repair and carried on to the top of the hill.

The crew battled on across bleak Exmoor, but more troubles faced them. When they reached Ashton Gate, it became obvious that the lanes were too narrow for the carriage to fit through. At this moment, the crew were beginning to think that the task was hopeless. But, still undeterred, Jack ordered the boat to be taken off the carriage, and the carriage to be sent across the moor to meet up with them two miles further on. Meanwhile, the crew pulled and hauled the boat over wooden rails, through the narrow lanes.

After hours of gruelling work, cutting down trees, tearing down walls, ditches and hedges to pull the boat through, they finally reached the top of Porlock Hill, one of the steepest hills in England.

'We shall never hold her back,' one crew member said, when he saw how steep the hill was. But despite all the odds, they got the lifeboat round the sharp u-bend and down the hill, arriving in Porlock Bay around 7am on the morning of the thirteenth. There in the bay was the stricken Forest Hall, helplessly being tossed about by the raging storm.

With the help of another tug boat that had come to help, the men of the Lynmouth lifeboat managed to attach ropes to the Forest Hall, and tow her to safety at Barry. The men were tired and hungry but triumphant. These heroic men had survived the worst weather conditions imaginable and saved the entire crew of the Forest Hall. They each received £5 and a watch for their efforts!

The recount of the rescue of the Forest Hall by the Lynmouth lifeboat is written in chronological order (the correct order in which the events happened).

Make a flow chart on the back of this sheet to show the sequence of events. The first two events are shown for you.

> **Telegraph message received. Forest Hall in distress.**

↓

> **Jack checks the launching ramp and says they must launch from Porlock.**

Clover Activity Centre - Diary
by Ann Bean

Mon Bus late leaving - 9.15 - Colin overslept, had to wait for him. Sat with Myra on coach. Stopped at Stonehenge for lunch - big, old rocks piled on top of each other. Lunch - cheese sandwiches, salt and vinegar crisps, choc biscuits, satsuma, blackcurrant drink.
1.45 Colin sick all over Michael. Miss Spiggot cleared up mess -yuk! Arrived at Clover Centre, big old house, looks spooky.
Sharing room with Myra, Tamsin and Meena.
Planning midnight feast!!

Tues Very tired no sleep last night kept hearing weird noises.
Morning - climbing wall - brilliant, I got to top.
Afternoon, walk along beach, found a fossil.
Colin fell in sea. Planning midnight feast.

Wed No midnight feast as we all fell asleep.
Morning - Archery - missed every time, Myra scored 2 bull's eyes.
Lunch beefburgers, chips, beans - best so far.
PM treasure trail round centre - clues too hard - came 5th
Evening, man brought in snakes to show - hid behind Meena.

Thurs Woke up at 5am - missing Mum. Myra cheered me up - home tomorrow.
Day out to Wildlife Park - FANTASTIC
Wolves were best, Lions all asleep.
Bought 2 pencils with zebras on and a postcard.
Slept on coach back to centre.
Evening - brilliant disco, wore jeans and blue top.

Fri Packing up, cleaning room. Said goodbye to staff, cried when we left.
Colin missed the coach - in loo - had to go back for him.
Boring journey home, fell asleep.
Back at school 4.30pm.

Name   The Lynmouth Lifeboat

The first paragraph of **The Lynmouth Lifeboat** is written large and in bold. What effect does this have?

_____

_____

There are many connectives (connecting words) in the account of the Lynmouth Lifeboat. Go through the text again and underline or highlight all the connecting words or phrases.
Make a list of all the connecting words or phrases you have found.

_____

_____

_____

_____

There are a few words in the text that are particularly used in the context of boats and lifeboats.
Use the text and a dictionary to work out the meaning of these words.

force 8 _____

_____

coxswain _____

_____

launching ramp _____

_____

tug _____

_____

Look at the notes that Ann has written in her diary about her week at Clover Activity Centre. At the weekend, she decides to write to her best friend and tell her all about her week. Write Ann's recount of her trip.
Remember to have:

- ✎   an introductory paragraph
- ✎   the events in the correct order
- ✎   paragraphs
- ✎   good linking words and phrases
- ✎   the simple past tense
- ✎   detail to add interest
- ✎   concluding paragraph to say how she felt about the whole week

This unit addresses the Literacy Strategy:
Term 1 objective 22: to read and evaluate a range of instructional texts in terms of their: purposes; organisation and layout; clarity and usefulness.

Making Your Own Worm Farm - a guide for farmers

An easy and fun way to recycle your organic
kitchen waste into garden compost.
Built entirely from reused and recycled materials.

You will need:

- Old carpet or sacking
- 3 car tyres
- Yellow pages or old bricks
- A piece of corrugated iron (60 x 60cm)
- Small piece of thick black polythene
  (old silage wrap if available)
- 30 newspapers
- An old pot or bucket
- A piece of wood or old hub cap to use as a lid
- Lots of Red Worms (These can be found in compost
  heaps and in horse manure.)
- Scraps of kitchen waste

Diagram for Making a Worm Farm

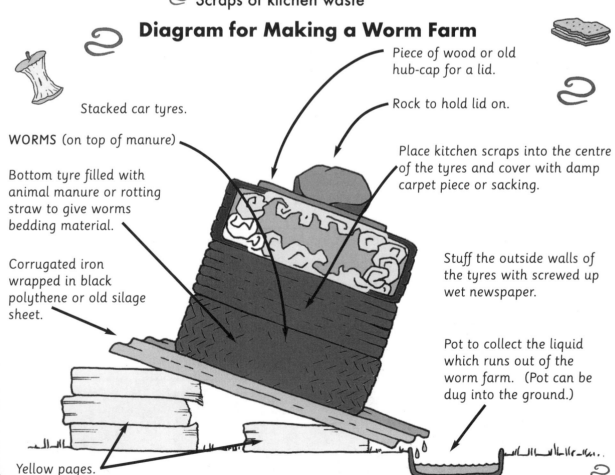

Piece of wood or old hub-cap for a lid.

Rock to hold lid on.

Stacked car tyres.

WORMS (on top of manure)

Place kitchen scraps into the centre of the tyres and cover with damp carpet piece or sacking.

Bottom tyre filled with animal manure or rotting straw to give worms bedding material.

Corrugated iron wrapped in black polythene or old silage sheet.

Stuff the outside walls of the tyres with screwed up wet newspaper.

Pot to collect the liquid which runs out of the worm farm. (Pot can be dug into the ground.)

Yellow pages.

More Information

Food:

Feed the worms with fruit and vegetables and any other kitchen scraps (NO MEAT). Their favourite food is banana skins and apple cores but they don't like too much orange peel, and too much bread is a bit dry for them. If you give them too much food at once the worm farm will get smelly as the excess food will start to go mouldy, so a few scraps every day would be sufficient.

Ideal Conditions:

Place your worm farm in a fairly sunny spot. It is best to put your worm farm near to the back door so that you can use it easily. You shouldn't let it get too wet or too dry. Don't let the cover of hessian or wet newspaper dry out. If the worm farm gets too wet, not enough air can get in, so it will smell. Solve this by adding some dry newspaper and feeding less often while the worms eat the newspaper.

White Worms:

White worms (they look very thin and white) are not really a problem but you can get rid of them if you want to by putting slices of bread into the worm farm. The white worms will gather on the bread and then you can remove it. Tea bags are good for keeping the white worms away as they do not like them.

1. What is the diagram for?

   _____

   _____

2. Why would someone want to make a worm farm?

   _____

   _____

3. Use a dictionary to find out the meaning of the word *organic*.

   _____

   _____

4. Why do you think that you can only put organic waste into the worm farm?

   _____

   _____

5. Circle the things that you think you can put in the worm farm:

   newspapers   **empty tins**   **felt pens**   **leaves**   **banana skins**

   apple cores   **smelly fish**   **yoghurt pots**   **tea bags**

   milk bottles   **meat bones**   **dead flowers**

7.   Use the information in the diagram to write the procedure for someone to make
a worm farm. Use these phrases to help you.

1. First you...   2. Secondly...   3. Then...   4. Next you... , etc.

_____

_____

_____

_____

_____

_____

_____

_____

_____

_____

8.   Would your procedure or the diagram be more useful for someone wanting to
make a worm farm?

_____

9.   Why do you think this? _____

_____

10.   How is the 'You will need' section organised?

_____

11.   It may have been more helpful to list the items in the order that they are used.
Reorganise the list into the order that the items would be needed.

1. _____

2. _____

3. _____

4. _____

5. _____

6. _____

7. _____

8. _____

9. _____

10. _____

Name

Making Your Own Worm Farm

12. Imagine you can take photos of someone as they are making a worm farm. Draw a series of pictures showing what photos you would take and write a short caption by the side of each one.

1

2

3

4

5

YEAR **5** | UNIT **10** | Sheet **A**   **Name**   Myths and Fables

PERSEUS AND MEDUSA

A long time ago on the island of Seriphos, in Greece, there lived a king called Polydectes. One day, a woman and her child were washed up on the shore of the island. The woman's name was Danae and the boy was called Perseus. The king soon fell in love with Danae, but she did not love him, as he was a cruel tyrant. Polydectes decided that he wanted to marry Danae, but knew that Perseus would never allow this to happen, so he hatched an evil plan. He announced that he was to be married to a different woman, and invited everyone to the wedding banquet. When Perseus arrived without a wedding present, (which the king knew he would, as Perseus was very poor), the king pretended to be furious and made Perseus feel so embarrassed that he promised the king that he could have any present that he wanted. The king was delighted, as this was exactly what he had planned.

"Anything?" asked Polydectes.

"Whatever you desire, Sire," replied Perseus.

"Then, I wish you to bring me the head of the Gorgon!" screamed the king.

At the sound of that name, the whole court fell silent as they realised the trick that Polydectes had played on Perseus. The Gorgon was a fearsome creature and Perseus would not return alive. There were three Gorgons, all sisters, all hideous. Only the sister called Medusa was mortal and could be killed, so this was the one that Perseus decided to seek.

Perseus travelled for many months searching for Medusa but with no luck. One evening whilst he was sitting miserably by his campfire, a beautiful woman stepped out of the flames. He knew at once that she was Athene, goddess of wisdom. She told Perseus that she had come to help him. She explained to Perseus that what Polydectes had not told him was that whoever looked at Medusa was turned instantly to stone. Carefully and quietly she outlined a plan to show Perseus how he could kill Medusa without being turned to stone. She gave him her gleaming shield and told him to go to the nearby bog to ask the Grey Ones where he could find Medusa.

The Grey Ones were three sisters, all born with grey hair, who shared only one tooth and one eye between them. Perseus crept up on them and snatched away both the tooth and the eye. He forced them to tell him where to find Medusa, before he would give back their eye and tooth.

Perseus knew that he was getting near to the cave where the Grey Ones had told him he would find Medusa, for all about him were figures of people who had looked at Medusa and been turned to stone. Perseus walked bravely into the cave and called out to Medusa.

Now, Athene had instructed Perseus only to look at the reflection of Medusa in the gleaming shield and that way he would not be turned to stone. As Perseus gazed at the reflection, he saw her green skin and glistening, red eyes. Her sharp, yellow teeth curved out of her mouth like tusks, but worst of all were the slimy, silver and green snakes, writhing and hissing from her head. Perseus was terrified but he was tempted to look at the monstrous creature. However, he resisted and, with a mighty cry, he swung his sword and felt it bite through the flesh. The ghastly head rolled to the back of the cave, and using only the reflection to guide him, he wrapped it in a cloth.

After many more adventures, Perseus arrived back at Seriphos, only to find that his mother had been made a washer woman in the palace as she had refused to marry King Polydectes. Perseus marched confidently into the throne room to confront the king. Polydectes was amazed to see that Perseus had returned, and was apparently unharmed.

"I bring you the Gorgon's head," declared Perseus.

But the king did not believe him and asked to see the head. As Perseus unveiled it, the king gasped with astonishment. That was the last sound he ever made, as he was instantly turned to stone.

Perseus lived a long, happy life and eventually became king of another land.

Aesop's Fables

Fable 1. A dog who loved eating eggs saw a round shape down by the sea. He gulped it down, thinking it was an egg. It was in fact a shellfish, and the weight in his stomach gave him terrible pains.

Fable 2. There was once a jackdaw who thought that he was better than his fellow jackdaws, because he was bigger than them. He decided to ask the crows if he could live with them. The crows, however, did not like the look of him, and chased him away. He returned to his fellow jackdaws, but they were so insulted by him that they would not have him back.

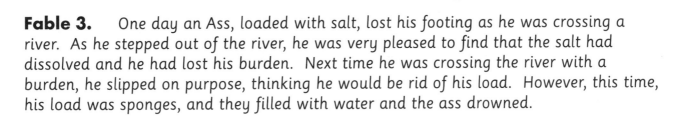

Fable 3. One day an Ass, loaded with salt, lost his footing as he was crossing a river. As he stepped out of the river, he was very pleased to find that the salt had dissolved and he had lost his burden. Next time he was crossing the river with a burden, he slipped on purpose, thinking he would be rid of his load. However, this time, his load was sponges, and they filled with water and the ass drowned.

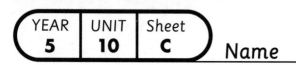

YEAR	UNIT	Sheet
5	10	C

Name _____   Myths and Fables

A **myth** is a story that takes place in ancient times or in an unknown time, and does not refer to any true historical events. Myths often include gods, goddesses and strange powers. A **legend** is a story that is also from a time long ago, but is often about things that may be historical. The tale of Robin Hood is a legend, as there may have actually been a real character similar to the one in the story. Both myths and legends deal with stories of good triumphing over evil and have heroes (usually men) and monsters to be overcome. The story of Perseus is a myth, as we have no historical evidence for any characters or events like the ones in the story.

1. Who is the hero in this story? _____

2. What is the monster called? _____

3. Who was the goddess? _____

4. How do we know from the text that Perseus is the hero?

    _____

    _____

5. Read through the story of Perseus and Medusa, and underline/highlight any words or phrases that describe the monster.
    Now write a description of the monster.

    _____

    _____

    _____

    _____

6. Put these sentences in the correct order using the boxes below:

    1. Polydectes, the king, wanted to marry Danae, and ordered Perseus to bring him the Gorgon's head to get Perseus out of the way.

    2. Perseus showed the king the head of Medusa and the king was turned to stone.

    3. The Grey Ones told Perseus where to find Medusa.

    4. Perseus and his mother, Danae, were washed up on a Greek island.

    5. The goddess, Athene, appeared to Perseus and told him how to kill Medusa, without being turned to stone.

    6. Perseus cut off the Medusa's head by looking at the reflection in the shield.

beginning							end

7. You have now made a summary of the story. On a separate piece of paper, draw a cartoon for each of the six points to tell the story of Perseus and Medusa.

A **fable** is a tale with a moral to teach. It tries to tell you how you should behave. Each of the three Aesop's Fables shown on Sheet B has a different moral.

8. Read the fables again and then match the story with the moral.

    1. **Things are not always what they seem.** **Fable** ☐

    2. **You can sometimes be too clever.** **Fable** ☐

    3. **Be content with what you have or you may end up with nothing.** **Fable** ☐

Aesop was a Greek slave who lived in the 6th century BC. He told fables that had animals as the main characters. These stories were told orally over hundreds of years and only written down much later.

9. Choose one of the morals below and write a fable about an animal, or animals, to teach the moral. When you have finished, give your fable to your partner, to see if they know which moral you are trying to teach. Rehearse telling your fable so that you can perform it to the class.
    Start on this page, but you may need to complete your fable on the back of this sheet.

    Even the weakest can find ways to be strong.

    Cheats never do well.

    Don't make too much out of a small problem.

    A small precaution can save you from a disaster.

    Working as a group can make the task easier.

    _____

    _____

    _____

    _____

    _____

    _____

    _____

    _____

    _____

This unit addresses the Literacy Strategy:
Term 2 objective   4: to read a range of narrative poems.
Term 2 objective   5: to perform poems in a variety of ways.

YEAR 5	UNIT 11	Sheet A

Name

Narrative Poem

The Strangers

Captain Dane, the famous explorer,
Was fearless brave and bold.
He left the planet, near the pole,
Adventure to unfold.
Was it to be?
Read on and see.

The world he left was peaceful,
No sickness or problems of war.
So easy was life it was boring;
The adventurer longed for much more.
So where would we go?
Very soon you will know.

He headed to many far planets
New species for to find.
He'd treat the aliens with respect,
Courteously and kind.
Was the voyage long?
To find out - read on.

With Captain Dane there travelled
A brave and trusty crew,
Interplanetary travellers,
Honourable and true.
What would they find?
They didn't mind.

The ship was called the 'Hawksbill',
A totally new type of craft.
It flew through the air in silence,
An interplanetary raft.
Would it take them far?
At least to a star.

The 'Hawksbill' could great distance travel.
In light years three score plus ten
Imperative for their survival
To return to their planet then.
Would they return?
We have yet to learn.

Tediously they journeyed
For nearly nine years more than ten.
When a cry could be heard from the
                                    console.
It was chief navigator, Jen.
What did she shout?
Next we'll find out.

"Look Captain, here on my scanners
Are signals I've recently seen.
From down there on yonder green planet
Life forms have shown up on the screen."
What had she found?
There was life, small and round.

Captain Dane led a small landing party,
Engineer, translator and others.
Optimistically all headed forward
To greet the new life forms like brothers.
Were they foolish or wise?
This would change their lives.

Confusion ensued on the hillside
Where the small landing party were
                                    standing.
No living thing could be seen anywhere
Near to the site of the landing.
What had happened here?
It will become clear.

They searched high and low for some
hours
Before they heard Captain Dane shout,
"It's no good, there's nothing here for us!
Let's return to our craft and fly out."
Did they leave there alone?
We'll soon be shown.

So they continued their journey
Disappointed they hadn't found life.
Pleased as they'd found other treasures.
Little did they imagine their strife.
Why should they have concern?
Continue, to learn.

Remember they went to the planet
That they landed upon in verse ten.
Where they couldn't find alien life forms
But the aliens soon had found them.
Had they hidden away?
'Twas a memorable day.

On that planet there really were life forms
Though not to be seen with the eye.
Microscopic they were, and quite friendly.
They saw the explorers walk by.
Did they try to make friends?
Read on to the end.

They couldn't shout very loudly,
Or climb far, as they were so small,
But the tread of space shoes was quite
comfy
To cling to, preventing a fall.
Where next would they go?
Progress upwards was slow.

The 'Hawksbill' continued its journey,
Full of adventure and fears
Treasures were found aplenty
During the next twenty years.
They then travelled home,
No longer to roam.

Dane was not welcomed back as a hero,
Though brave and fearlessly bold.
For the aliens stuck to the soles of his feet
Gave the people at home nasty colds.
No one was well
Sadly to tell.

So remember if you go exploring,
That all may seem well when it's not.
So take every safety precaution
Or you could end up in a tight spot.
Avoid all dangers
Beware of strangers!

1. How many lines are in each verse of the poem? _____

2. What do you notice in line five of each of the first fifteen verses?

    _____

    _____

3. How many verses are there in the poem? _____

4. What is different about the last verse?

    _____

    _____

5. Describe the noise made by 'Hawksbill' as it flew.

    _____

    _____

6. Give the name and job of the only two characters actually named in the poem.

    _____

    _____

7. On the lines below write the lines spoken by Jen in the poem.

    _____

    _____

    _____

    _____

8. What would you say the moral of the story is?

    _____

    _____

    _____

9. The text is a 'narrative poem'. Explain what that means.

    _____

    _____

10. Write the story of the poem in prose. You might want to add extra details or
    expand the information about the main characters. Illustrate your story.

11. Describe how any verse of the poem is structured - be as detailed as you can.

_____

_____

_____

_____

_____

12. Write a short definition of each of the following words found in the poem.

species _____

_____

interplanetary _____

_____

honourable _____

_____

imperative _____

_____

tediously _____

_____

microscopic _____

_____

13a. Did you enjoy the poem? _____

  b. Give reasons for your answer.

_____

_____

14. Write one (or two) more verses about an event that happened
    during the journey. Use all you know about the structure of the poem.

EXTRA ACTIVITY
In groups find an effective way to perform the poem.

This unit addresses the Literacy Strategy:
Term 1 objective   3: to investigate how characters are presented, referring to text; through dialogue, action and description; how the reader responds to them (as victims, heroes, etc.); through examining their relationships with other characters.
Term 2 objective   8: to distinguish between the author and the narrator, investigating narrative viewpoint and the treatment of different characters, e.g. minor characters, heroes, villains, and perspectives of the action from different characters.
Term 3 objective   2: to identify the point of view from which a story is told and how this affects the reader's response.

Jack's Story

Well I guess you all know the story about how I climbed the beanstalk, and stole the greedy giant's gold. But there are a few things about which I need to set the record straight. I am definitely not thick or stupid. I suppose, at first sight, swopping our cow for five beans, might look a little daft, but I had my reasons.

I don't know why my mum wanted to sell Daisy, our cow, but off I set to market, one sunny, Saturday morning. The young lady (no, it wasn't a little, old man - they always get that wrong) that stepped out of the bushes at Waterloo Cross was quite a 'looker,' I have to say. She said her name was Karis and when she suggested swopping Daisy for these five beans she had, I thought at first, 'you've got to be joking'. One of the many gifts I do have, however, (besides being devastatingly handsome) is a strong intuition (ask your teacher what that means). When I saw those beans, they seemed to shine like gold and I thought, 'yeah, let's take a chance'. Besides, it gave me a chance to talk to Karis a bit longer.

Of course, when I got home, Mum went ballistic and did the weeping and wailing, 'bed, no dinner,' routine. She threw the beans clean out the window, and stormed off to visit her friend, Beryl.

Well, the next morning, my room was kind of darker than usual, and when I looked up, I saw these leaves all over my window. I managed to push it open and realised that the beans had grown a beanstalk right up to the sky. Well I tell you, that beanstalk was really difficult to climb. It was rough and hairy and had shoots going off all over the place. Anyway, eventually I got to what seemed like the top, way up in the clouds.

Looking around me, I saw this gigantic castle thing and I mean

gigantic.

I hadn't ever seen anything like that before. So, I made my way there and peeped in at the door. I am not joking, I nearly fell over. There was this guy, he must have been ten metres tall and ugly as sin, counting all these bags of gold. I could hear him booming, 'I need more, I must get more!' I thought, 'well he's a greedy guts,' and I didn't think twice when I saw my chance to nip in and steal one of the bags of gold.

Mum was pretty pleased, to say the least, when she saw the gold, and life was really good for a long time. Then, one day, Mum told me that all the gold had gone, and did I think I could manage to go up the beanstalk again? Well I didn't fancy meeting old giant features again but Mum seemed pretty desperate. So off I set again, hacking my way through the jungle of leaves.

This time, I saw the big fellah, sitting there talking to a harp, telling it what music he wants, like it's some magic C.D. player. On the table, there's this huge hen just laying an egg - a golden egg! I thought to myself, if we had that hen, then we wouldn't ever run out of gold and Mum would always be happy. So, when I saw my chance, I lifted the hen and I thought the harp might come in handy to impress Karis (I'd been seeing quite a lot of her lately).

Now, the harp was my mistake because as soon as I picked it up, it started shouting blue murder. I legged it down the beanstalk but I could hear the giant hot on my heels. I've never moved so fast in my life. I reached the bottom, grabbed next door's chain-saw, and sliced my way through that beanstalk before you could say 'Jack and the Beanstalk'. They always get this part wrong as well, because there wasn't any flying, dead, ten metre giant that landed in our garden. I guess he must have changed his mind about chasing me.

So, how did it all turn out? Well, happily ever after, of course.

Jack's Mum's Story

I was at my wits end to know what to do. We had sold everything that was worth anything, but we still owed the rent for the cottage. Baron Snicklebaum had been round last night, and he was none too pleased that I couldn't pay the rent. He said we had three days to pay up, or we were out on the street.

I knew Jack loved our cow, Daisy, but she really was the only thing we had left to sell. Jack was a bit of a dreamer and a bit strange looking, but I thought they might take pity on him, at market, and give him a good price for Daisy.

When Jack came back with just five miserable beans, I realised just what an idiot he really was. I couldn't believe that he had swopped Daisy for FIVE BEANS! I was furious, and desperate to work out how we were going to pay the rent this month. My only hope was my friend, Beryl, who had helped us out with a loan a few times before. I didn't like borrowing money, but what choice had we got? We had no food in the house, so I sent Jack to bed, poor lad. I thought if he was asleep, he wouldn't notice how hungry he was.

Beryl hadn't been able to help, and I had just decided we would have to go and stay with my sister and her ten kids, when Jack arrived home all breathless, with this bag of gold and some story about a giant he had met up in the clouds. To be honest, I thought he had gone totally mad but I didn't ask too many questions, because there was this bag of gold on the table, and our worries were over.

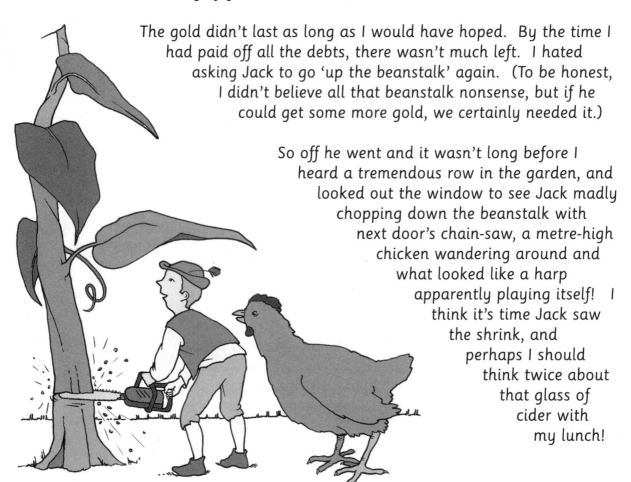

The gold didn't last as long as I would have hoped. By the time I had paid off all the debts, there wasn't much left. I hated asking Jack to go 'up the beanstalk' again. (To be honest, I didn't believe all that beanstalk nonsense, but if he could get some more gold, we certainly needed it.)

So off he went and it wasn't long before I heard a tremendous row in the garden, and looked out the window to see Jack madly chopping down the beanstalk with next door's chain-saw, a metre-high chicken wandering around and what looked like a harp apparently playing itself! I think it's time Jack saw the shrink, and perhaps I should think twice about that glass of cider with my lunch!

The Giant's Story

'I need more, I must get more!' Well that's what that boy heard. I wanted at least thirty bags of gold to pay for the new hospital that we desperately needed. The old one was falling down, and everyone was relying on me to come up with the money to pay for it. My hen, Edith, had been working overtime trying to produce more golden eggs, but it really was only one every three months that was golden. That would mean it would take another six years to get enough money to build the hospital. I had to think of something else.

I was sure there had been twenty bags of gold last time I had counted, but now there were only nineteen. I must have made a mistake, which made things worse. Now it would be nine years before I had enough for the hospital. Still, today was the day that Edith would produce another golden egg. She liked to listen to the harp playing. It soothed her nerves, and we sat together, waiting.

As soon as she had laid it, I hurried to lock it away. I really did think there were twenty bags and I was worried there might be thieves about. As I was returning to Edith, I heard my harp screaming, and Edith squawking in the distance. The front door was open, and half way down the road, I could see a small figure running like mad, with the harp under one arm, and Edith, flapping madly, under the other. As I watched, the boy seemed to be climbing into a bush, and disappearing down below the ground. I didn't panic as I knew that I could reach him with a few steps. But when I looked at the bush, I realised that, actually, it was the top of a long plant that disappeared down and down. As I peered down, my knees began to shake and my head spin. Now, I didn't mind fighting dragons, crossing raging rivers, rescuing fair princesses from the hands of ugly ogres, but the one thing I am really scared of, is heights. When I saw that beanstalk going down and down, I knew there was no way I was going down it. Sadly I walked back to the castle to dream up other ways to raise the money for the hospital. Perhaps I could visit Dragon Dreadlock and 'borrow' a few of his treasures.

Jack and
the Beanstalk

These three versions of 'Jack and the Beanstalk' are told from different viewpoints.
Each of the characters has knowledge or interest in different parts and details of the
story.

1. What events or information do the following characters know about, that other
    characters do not know?

    Jack _____

    _____

    _____

    The Giant _____

    _____

    _____

    Jack's Mum _____

    _____

    _____

2. In Jack's story, he is the narrator and we learn about his character through his
    eyes. What do you learn about Jack's character from his story?

    _____

    _____

    _____

3. What evidence do you have from the text to show this?

    _____

    _____

    _____

4. How does this version of the story make you feel about Jack?

    _____

    _____

    _____

5. What do we learn about Jack's character from his Mum's story?

    _____

    _____

    _____

YEAR	UNIT	Sheet
5	**12**	**F**

Name

Jack and
the Beanstalk

6. What evidence from the text do you have to show this?

    _____

    _____

    _____

7. How does this version make you feel about Jack?

    _____

    _____

    _____

8. The way we view the story of Jack and the Beanstalk is changed depending on
    which voice is narrating the story; this is called the 'narrative voice'. Our view of
    the giant is completely different, depending on which 'voice' we listen to.
    What is your opinion of the giant after reading Jack's Story?

    _____

    _____

    _____

9. What is your opinion of the giant after reading The Giant's Story?

    _____

    _____

    _____

10. The author of the story is the person that writes the story, and can also be the
    narrative voice. If the author writes with his 'voice', not the 'voice' of one of the
    characters, then he can invent and write information and details about all the
    characters.

    Write the story of
    Jack and the
    Beanstalk as if you
    are the author.

    You can change
    details and
    characters, but
    keep mainly to the
    original story and
    remember, you are
    not in the story.

I Was Feeling...

1.

I was feeling sick and dizzy. It had been a very close shave when they had nearly found me crouching in the corner of the alleyway. There had been four of them altogether, big and hairy. They looked just like they had walked out of a Treasure Island book and I had no intention of letting them find out that I knew about their wicked plans. Then suddenly I remembered and, as my memory came back to me, I felt tingles of fear creep up my spine. I had left my cap on the table...

2.

I was feeling sick and dizzy. Fortunately my Invisishield had prevented them from detecting me in the corner of the alleyway. There had been four of them altogether, big and scaly with breath like rotting fungus. I knew they were Zargons planning to take over our planet and I knew that the future of our world depended on what I did next. Then suddenly I remembered and, as my memory came back to me, I felt a tingle of fear creep up my spine. I had left my transporter on the table...

3.

I was feeling sick and dizzy. I had crawled behind a battered dolls' house in the corner of the damp cellar and held my breath. In the moonlit darkness the four dark shapes searched for me, only their red glowing eyes betrayed their presence. I knew they could smell my blood and it was only a matter of time before they found me. Then suddenly I remembered and, as my memory came back to me, I felt tingles of fear creep up my spine. I had left my torch on the table...

4.

I was feeling sick and dizzy. Michael Armstrong had actually noticed me. He had actually spoken to me and smiled! I curled up in the corner of the classroom just to savour the moment, to relive that one precious smile. This had to be the best day of my life. I couldn't tell the other girls, they would only laugh at me, saying I was imagining it. I could just hear their sneering voices -
"Why would he look at you, spot face?" Then suddenly, as my thoughts came back to me, I realised I had left my diary on my desk...

5.

I was feeling sick and dizzy. It had been a very close shave when they unexpectedly turned into the alleyway. I had been following the four of them for days now and thought I knew their plans. I had ducked down into the putrid rubbish behind the overflowing bins as they sauntered past me. However, an overheard snatch of their conversation gave me another piece of the jigsaw. The robbery was to be tonight and I had no time to lose. I must warn the Armstrongs. Then suddenly I remembered and I felt tingles of panic creep up my spine. I had left my mobile on the table...

1. Which genre is each story opening written in? Choose from these:

   Horror   Romance   Adventure   Newspaper Report
   Ghost Stories   Science Fiction   Fantasy   Detective   Humour

   1. _____   2. _____

   3. _____   4. _____

   5. _____

2. Make a list of the words and phrases that give you clues about what type of
    genre the extract is written in.

Extract 1_____

   _____

   _____

   _____

Extract 2_____

   _____

   _____

   _____

Extract 3_____

   _____

   _____

   _____

Extract 4_____

   _____

   _____

   _____

Extract 5_____

   _____

   _____

3.   Choose one of the genres that you are familiar with and record some of its special features.

   a. **Type of genre.** (What kind of story is it?) _____

   b. **Characters.** (What type of characters are usually in these stories?)

   _____

   _____

   c. **Setting.** (Where and when do these stories usually take place?)

   _____

   _____

   d. **Atmosphere.** (Are there special words used to create the feeling of the place?)

   _____

   _____

   e. **Plot.** (What kind of things usually happen in these stories?)

   _____

   _____

   f. **Special Details.** (Are there special objects used in this type of story?)

   _____

   _____

4.   Look at extract 1. Explain what the author means by:

   'It had been a very close shave'

   _____

   _____

   'They looked just like they had walked out of a Treasure Island book'

   _____

   _____

5.   Look at extract 3. Explain what the author means by:

   'betrayed their presence'

   _____

   _____

   'only a matter of time'

   _____

   _____

6. Look at extract 4. What does the author mean by:

    'to savour the moment'

    _____

    _____

7. What tells us that the other girls didn't like the writer?

    _____

    _____

8. Look at extract 5. Underline the correct meaning for these words and phrases.

putrid:	useless	smelly	rotting	pile
sauntered:	walked quickly	crept	walked slowly	ran
piece of the jigsaw:	idea	part of the plan	game word	

9. What was the item left on the table in each of the extracts?

    Extract 1 _____

    Extract 2 _____

    Extract 3 _____

    Extract 4 _____

    Extract 5 _____

10. Choose 5 different items that could have been left on the table. Make sure they match the genre.

    Extract 1 _____

    Extract 2 _____

    Extract 3 _____

    Extract 4 _____

    Extract 5 _____

11. Choose your favourite extract and continue the story.

This unit addresses the Literacy Strategy:
Term 2 objective 10: to understand the differences between literal and figurative language, e.g. through discussing the effects of imagery in poetry and prose.

YEAR 5 | UNIT 14 | Sheet A

Name

Imagery

SNOW

Second by second, the white blanket grew
On the midnight garden.
Softening its angles into curves.

The snow, silent like a ballerina
Dancing through the trees,
Landing like breath on the branches.

The trees stood veiled like brides,
Their fingers, weighted down,
Waiting for their groom to free them.

The groom lingered silently in the shadows.
Not yet time for him to claim his bride.
For Spring was his name.

WINTER

Winter was a loving child,
Clinging to her mother Earth.
Only reluctant would she depart.

Sometimes in temper,
She raged about her mother's knees
Destroying all that she loved.

And then in sorrow,
For her violent rage, her icy tears,
Would flood the ravaged land.

Until the calm descent,
Of pure white flakes,
Stealthily settled her to sleep once more.

Summer Holiday

Kirsten eagerly pulled back the curtains to welcome the new day.

Yesterday had been a golden day full of sparkling, silver sand and emerald seas lapping at her feet. The heat had wrapped itself about her like a warm blanket. The best way, the only way to start a holiday.

To her dismay, the sight that met her eyes was grey and dismal. She glared out of her window in disbelief. The sky was an overcast and gloomy giant. The trees that ran alongside the park were whipping about in the lashing wind. As she watched, leaves rushed and swirled, chasing round the shivering trees.

Around the lake, the small wooden boats knocked and jostled together, as they strained against their moorings. Already one had broken free, and could be seen in the distance only as a red and green smudge, bobbing frantically up and down in the breath of the storm, like a swimmer in distress.

The sea of grass, that yesterday was covered with sprawling holiday makers, now rippled like waves in the wind. Only a couple of foolhardy kids, with plastic macs and wellies, had braved the swirling weather this morning. They were fighting their way across the park, and Kirsten was barely able to make out their wind-tossed screams of delight.

Just as she was thinking that, maybe a really windy day could be fun, the rain began. At first it was only a few spots that landed, plop, on her window pane, but that soon turned to a streaming river that blurred the glass and made her view of the world nothing but a streaky vision of blues and greens. Some holiday, she thought!

'Snow' and 'Winter' are both poems, whereas 'Summer Holiday' is a piece of prose. All three texts have strong images (pictures in your head). The images are created using different types of words and phrases.

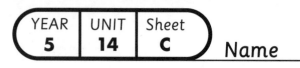

Name _____   Imagery

> **Simile**: A simile says something is **like** something else - it
> compares two things, e.g. 'Her lips were like a rosebud.'

1.   Read through the poem, 'Snow', and find two similes. Copy them out on the lines
     below.

     _____

     _____

2.   Write some endings for the sentences below to create similes of your own. Make
     sure your simile creates an appropriate image.

     The sun shining on the water was like _____

     _____

     The fox ran through the street like a _____

     _____

     The volcano erupted like _____

     _____

> **Metaphor**: A metaphor says something is something else,
> e.g. 'Her lips were shining rosebuds'.

3.   Read through the poem 'Winter' and find a metaphor. Copy it out on the line
     below.

     _____

4.   Why do you think that Winter was described as clinging to her mother?

     _____

5.   What type of weather do you think Winter's 'temper' was?

     _____

6.   What type of weather do you think her 'icy tears' were?

     _____

7.   What was it that settled Winter back to sleep again?

     _____

> **Personification**: Personification is a kind of metaphor. It links objects and
> feeling with humans or human actions or behaviour.
> e.g. 'Winter has packed her bags and gone away'. Here,
> winter is seen as a woman leaving home.

© Andrew Brodie Publications ✓ www.acblack.com

8. The whole of the poem 'Winter' is personification. Make a list of the human features that the poet has given to Winter.

Human Features

The snow _____

The trees _____

Spring _____

9. Look at the text called 'Summer Holiday'. It contains strong images of stormy weather. Find all the adjectives in the text that describe the following.

sand _____

sky _____

trees _____

boats _____

grass _____

holiday-makers _____

weather _____

10. Read through the passage again and underline/highlight two similes, and two metaphors or personifications. Write them on the lines below.

simile _____

simile _____

metaphor/personification _____

_____

metaphor/personification _____

_____

This unit addresses the Literacy Strategy:
Term 2 objective   15: to read a range of explanatory texts, investigating and noting features of impersonal style, e.g. complex sentences: use of passive voice; technical vocabulary; hypothetical language (if...then, might when the...); use of words/phrases to make sequential, causal, logical connections, e.g. while, during, after, because, after, due to, only when, so.

YEAR 5	UNIT 15	Sheet A	Name	The Ancient Egyptians

The Ancient Egyptians

The Ancient Egyptian art of embalming dead bodies, to preserve them for the future, is considered to be a remarkable achievement.

Firstly, bodies were taken to the 'Beautiful House' where the embalmers worked. A cut was made in the left side of the body using a flint knife. **Next** the liver, lungs and brain were taken out, and placed in special jars called 'canopic jars'. The organs were protected by the canopic jars, as the Ancient Egyptians believed that any part of your body could be used in a spell against you. It was believed that the heart must remain in the body, as this was needed to gain admittance to the afterlife. **Only when** these organs were removed, could the body be covered with natron crystals. Natron was used to dry out the body, and stop it from rotting. Sawdust or leaves was then packed into the body to keep its shape. Pads of linen were placed in the empty eye sockets, to replace the eyeballs, and then the eyelids were pulled down. Linen bandages were then wrapped around the body, ready for it to be put in the coffin. The wrapped body is known as a mummy.

If the person was rich, then the coffin might be made up of several layers. Each of these may have been painted and decorated. Paintings of gods, and spells written in hieroglyphs might decorate the outside of the coffin. The coffin was shaped roughly into a body shape, and a portrait of the dead person often decorated the head end of the coffin.

When the body was safely in the coffin, the family were allowed to see it. A label with a god painted on it was attached to the mummy. This identified the body and gave more protection from evil spells. The ceremony of the 'Opening of the Mouth' was considered to be one of the most important rites for the dead person. Special tools were used to open the mouth, and sacred liquids were poured in. Spells were spoken and incense burnt. It was believed that this would allow the dead person to eat, drink and move in the afterlife.

During the funeral, mourners were paid to wave their arms about, weep and throw dust over themselves. It was thought that the more mourners there were, the more honour the dead person had. It was believed that below the earth, there was another world called the Underworld, full of evil executioners, perilous lakes, fires and poisonous snakes.

As a result of this belief, the body was buried with a special book called The Book of the Dead which was written on papyrus. This book contained many spells which, when said, would keep away danger. A map of the Underworld, and information to help the person through the 'Weighing of the Heart' ceremony, were also written on the papyrus.

The ceremony of the weighing of the heart took place in the Hall of Two Truths. A pair of weighing scales were used to weigh the heart. The Egyptians believed that forty-two gods then asked the dead person questions about his life and accused him of evil deeds, which he denied. **If** he was thought to be telling the truth, **then** he was allowed through to the kingdom of Osiris. If he failed the test, then his heart was eaten by a goddess called the 'Devourer,' and he did not go on to the afterlife with Osiris. The bodies of 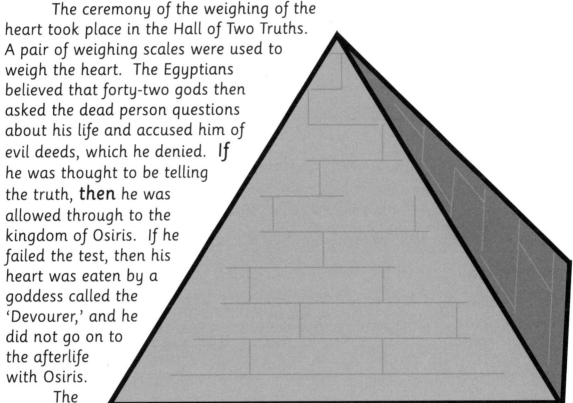 the Pharaohs were protected by placing them deep inside great pyramids of stone. Many objects were buried with the mummy in the tomb, as it was thought that these would be needed in the afterlife. These would include jewellery, furniture, clothing and models that were believed to spring to life when the dead person needed them in the afterlife.

Huge doors and passages with dead ends were built to try and stop robbers from stealing the rich offerings. **Despite** these precautions, nearly all the pyramids were robbed and their contents taken. **In later years**, the Pharaohs were buried in tombs set deep into the rock, and protected by guards but even these were robbed over the years.

▲ List three things that were done to the dead body in Ancient Egyptian times, before it was placed in the coffin.

1. _____

2. _____

3. _____

▲ Describe what the Egyptians thought the Underworld was like.

_____

_____

_____

▲ What happened to the dead person in the Hall of Two Truths?

_____

_____

_____

▲ In this text, several unusual words and terms are used that are relevant to the explanation about how Ancient Egyptians buried their dead. Find the words below in the text and write their meaning. You may find a dictionary helps or you may be able to work out the meaning from the text.

embalming _____

_____

canopic jars _____

_____

natron crystals _____

_____

hieroglyphs _____

_____

rites _____

_____

incense _____

_____

mourners _____

_____

▲ Look at these sentences taken from the text and then change them round so that they say the same thing but in a different way.
The first one has been done for you.

A cut was made in the left side of the body using a flint knife.

They made a cut in the left side of the body using a flint knife.

Natron was used to dry out the body and stop it from rotting.

The Ancient Egyptians used natron

Linen bandages were then wrapped around the body, ready for it to be put in the coffin.

They wrapped

A label with a god painted on it was attached to the mummy.

They attached

The ceremony of the 'Opening of the Mouth' was considered to be one of the most important rites for the dead person.

One of the most important

Special tools were used to open the mouth and sacred liquids were poured in.

The first sentence from the text was written in the passive voice, you have changed it to the active voice.

▲ Look at the words that are in bold in the text. What purpose do you think these words have? _____

▲ Find out as much as you can about Osiris or the 'Devourer' and write a paragraph explaining their roles in Ancient Egypt.

This unit addresses the Literacy Strategy:
Term 2 objective 17: to locate information confidently and efficiently through i) using contents, indexes, sections, headings ii) skimming to gain overall sense of text iii) scanning to locate specific information iv) close reading to aid understanding v) text marking vi) using CD ROM and other IT sources, where available.

YEAR 5	UNIT 16	Sheet A

Name

Skimming and Scanning

Lewis Carroll (1832-98)

Lewis Carroll is famous for writing the story of 'Alice's Adventures in Wonderland'. The name Lewis Carroll is a pseudonym; his real name was Charles Lutwidge Dodgson and he was a mathematics don at Christ Church College, which is part of Oxford University. He lived there for 47 years and was a shy, reserved man who loved telling stories to children.

The Dean, or Head, of the college at the time was Henry Liddell; he had a son called Harry and 3 daughters called Alice, Lorina and Edith. Charles Dodgson would love to sit in the gardens making up magical adventure stories for Alice. She was the heroine of the stories and her sisters appeared as the Lory and the Eaglet.

When Alice was 10 years old she begged Charles Dodgson to write the stories down for her. By Christmas 1864 the first manuscript of 'Alice's Adventures Underground' was finished. Everyone who saw it thought it should be published. The following summer, in 1865, three years after Alice had asked Charles Dodgson to write the stories down, Alice was given the first bound copy of the book. Dean Liddell had suggested that the book be re-titled 'Alice's Adventures in Wonderland', and so it was.

In 1871 other stories Dodgson had told the sisters were published under the title 'Through the Looking Glass and What Alice Found There'. The books were extremely successful and twenty years later, when Alice was married, he told her that he had sold well over 100,000 copies.

Like many other authors, Dodgson chose to use a pseudonym for his books. Lewis Carroll was derived from his mother's maiden name of Lutwidge, also his middle name, Lutwidge being the German for Lewis. Carroll came from the Latin for Charles which is Carolus.

Dodgson died in 1898 while he was staying with his sister in Guildford and he is buried there.

Alice's Adventures in Wonderland

by Lewis Carroll

Name _____

Skimming and Scanning

1. 'Skim' the passage about Lewis Carroll quickly for about a minute. Write down your overall view of what the passage is about.

_____

_____

_____

_____

2. 'Scan' the passage and find the answers to the following:

   a. The year of Lewis Carroll's birth [   ]

   b. The year of Lewis Carroll's death [   ]

   c. Lewis Carroll's real name [   ]

   d. Alice's surname [   ]

   e. The names of Alice's two sisters [   ]

   and [   ]

3. Read the passage closely and use a highlighter or underline with pencil, to pick out the key facts. You should now be able to answer the following questions.

   a) What was Charles Dodgson's occupation and where did he work?

   _____

   _____

   _____

   b) What is meant by the 'first manuscript' and what was Lewis Carroll's first manuscript called?

   _____

   _____

   _____

c) Who suggested the new title for Dodgson's first book and what was it?

_____

_____

_____

4.   What is the meaning of the following words? Use a dictionary if you need to.

pseudonym: _____

_____

_____

don: _____

_____

_____

heroine: _____

_____

_____

5.   If you were to choose a pseudonym what would it be and why?

_____

_____

_____

_____

_____

YEAR 5	UNIT 17	Sheet A

Name

The Happiest Day of My Life

The following short piece of writing was written by Holly, aged 10. She was given the title, 'The Happiest Day of my Life', and she was told that it could be a true account or fictitious.

I sat on the smooth tide-washed sand, looking out to sea at the red-orange light coming up from the east. It was of course, the sun. Its reflection shone onto the rippling waves, gently and peacefully. The sound of birds behind me brought me to stand. I looked around at the scaly palm trees on which were sprouting fresh, green leaves. The rocks on the sand were smooth and comfortable to sit on.

I thought sorrowfully, about my best friend, Kate, who I had lost on a tragic journey, here, to this, ...place. Tears filled my eyes and rolled down my cheeks. I'd do anything to see her again. I don't know what happened to Kate; I wish I knew. I sometimes thought I could hear Kate's voice, but it was too good to be true.

I slept a couple of nights here on this place; an island? I jumped onto a rock and sat down. This time I was absolutely sure I heard Kate's voice.

"Kate!" I called. "Kate where are you?"

And this time sure enough a face appeared in the trees, and this was too good to be true, it was Kate my greatest friend. We hugged and kissed each other. Our tears filled our eyes, this time for happiness. This surely was the happiest day of our lives.

The Happiest Day of My Life

1. Do you think the story 'The Happiest Day of My Life', was fiction or non-fiction? Give reasons for your answer.

2. How do you think the narrator arrived at the 'place' in the story? You may have more than one idea. Use your imagination.

3. Why do you think the narrator was not sure if she was on an island?

4. The first part of the story is descriptive.
   In the boxes below suggest other adjectives that Holly could have used to describe the sun, sand, waves and palm trees.

smooth, tide-washed sand	rippling waves
_____ sand	_____ waves
red orange light of the sun	scaly palm trees
_____ sun	_____ trees

5. How long had the narrator been in the 'place' in the story?

☐ one night ☐ three nights

☐ two nights ☐ four nights

6. How do you think Kate became separated from the narrator? Use your own ideas and write a suggestion in the box below.

7. Rewrite 'The Happiest Day of My Life' from Kate's viewpoint and call it 'Kate's Story'. You may use the writing frame provided on Sheet D.

The story could begin like this:

We jumped from the sinking boat together. Our life-jackets kept us afloat but the tide forced us apart.....

OR

When the engine failed on the small aircraft, the pilot yelled for us to jump. As I floated down towards the land I could see two other parachutes below me. One fell into the sea and the other somewhere in the large patch of trees......

Kate's Story....

_____

_____

_____

_____

_____

_____

_____

_____

_____

_____

_____

_____

_____

_____

_____

_____

_____

_____

_____

_____

_____

_____

_____

_____

_____

_____

_____

This unit addresses the Literacy Strategy:
Term 3 objective   6: to explore the challenge and appeal of older literature through: listening to older literature being read aloud; reading accessible poems, stories and extracts; reading extracts from classic serials shown on television; discussing differences in language used.
FOR ADVANCED READERS

YEAR 5	UNIT 18	Sheet A

Name   Oliver Twist 1

Oliver Twist is the story of an orphaned boy who was brought up in the workhouse - a place where very poor people lived and worked in bad conditions. Oliver was aged 9 and in this extract Oliver is chosen by the other hungry boys to ask for more food.

Oliver Twist
by Charles Dickens (1812 - 70)

A council was held; lots were cast who should walk up to the master after supper that evening, and ask for more; and it fell to Oliver Twist.

The evening arrived; the boys took their places. The master in his cook's uniform, stationed himself at the copper; his pauper assistants ranged themselves behind him; the gruel was served out; and a long grace was said over the short commons. The gruel disappeared; the boys whispered to each other, and winked at Oliver; while his neighbours nudged him. Child as he was, he was desperate with hunger, and reckless with misery. He rose from the table; and advancing to the master, basin and spoon in hand, said: somewhat alarmed at his own temerity:

"Please, sir, I want some more."

The master was a fat, healthy man; but he turned very pale. He gazed in stupefied astonishment on the small rebel for some seconds, and then clung for support to the copper. The assistants were paralysed with wonder; the boys with fear.

"What!" said the master at length, in a faint voice.

"Please, sir," replied Oliver, "I want some more."

The master aimed a blow at Oliver's head with the ladle; pinioned him in his arms; and shrieked aloud for the beadle.

The board were sitting in solemn conclave, when Mr. Bumble rushed into the room in great excitement, and addressing the gentleman in the high chair, said,

"Mr. Limbkins, I beg your pardon, sir! Oliver Twist has asked for more!"

There was a general start. Horror was depicted on every countenance.

"For more!" said Mr. Limbkins. "Compose yourself, Bumble, and answer me distinctly. Do I understand that he asked for more, after he had eaten the supper allotted by the dietary?"

"He did, sir," replied Bumble.

"That boy will be hung," said the gentleman in the white waistcoat. "I know that boy will be hung." …

… An animated discussion took place. Oliver was ordered into instant confinement; and a bill was next morning pasted on the outside of the gate, offering a reward of five pounds to anybody who would take Oliver Twist off the hands of the parish. In other words, five pounds and Oliver Twist were offered to any man or woman who wanted an apprentice to any trade, business, or calling.

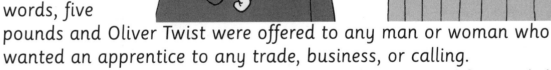

"I never was more convinced of anything in my life," said the gentleman in the white waistcoat, as he knocked at the gate and read the bill next morning: "I never was more convinced of anything in my life, than I am that that boy will come to be hung."

As I purpose to show in the sequel whether the white-waistcoated gentleman was right or not, I should perhaps mar the interest of this narrative (supposing it to possess any at all), if I ventured to hint just yet, whether the life of Oliver Twist had this violent termination or no.

Name _____   Oliver Twist 1

1.   Match the following words to their meaning. Use a dictionary to help you.

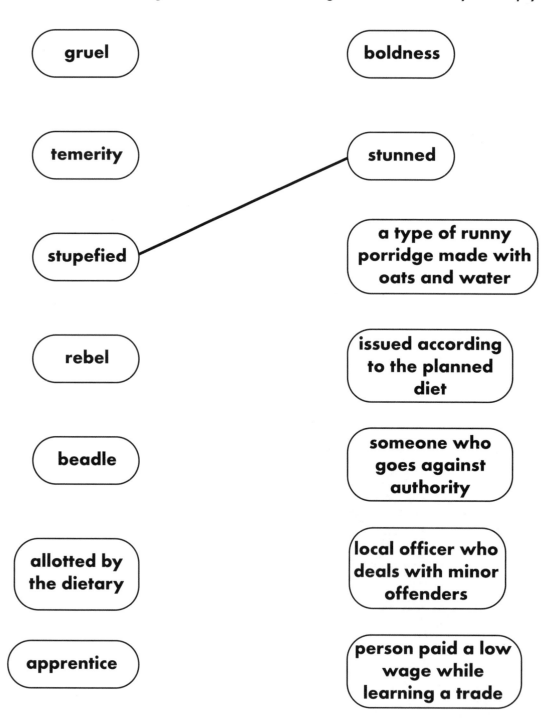

2.   Find two more words or phrases that were used in the passage which would not
      be used in a modern story and write their meanings.

1. _____ ➔ _____
                              _____

2. _____ ➔ _____
                              _____

3.   How did Oliver feel when he asked the master for more food?

      _____

      _____

      _____

4.   What was the master's reaction to Oliver's question?

      _____

      _____

      _____

5.   What is meant by, 'Oliver was ordered into instant confinement'?

      _____

      _____

      _____

6.   A bill or notice was pasted on the gate next morning. Explain, in your own words, what the notice said.

      _____

      _____

      _____

      _____

7.   Who is narrating in the last paragraph?

      ☐ **the gentleman in the white waistcoat**   ☐ **Oliver**

      ☐ **Mr Bumble**   ☐ **the author**

8.   What did the white-waistcoated gentleman say would happen to Oliver?

      _____

      _____

      _____

This unit addresses the Literacy Strategy:
Term 3 objective   6: to explore the challenge and appeal of older literature through: listening to older literature being read aloud; reading accessible poems, stories and extracts; reading extracts from classic serials shown on television; discussing differences in language used.
FOR ADVANCED READERS

YEAR | UNIT | Sheet
5 | **19** | **A**   Name   Oliver Twist 2

In this extract Oliver has watched his new 'friends', the Dodger and Master Bates, take a handkerchief from a gentleman's pocket, while he was at a bookstall and then run off. Oliver turned to run too...

Oliver Twist
by Charles Dickens (1812 - 70)

1 This was all done in a minute's space. In the very instant when Oliver began to run, the old gentleman, putting his hand in his pocket, and missing his handkerchief, turned sharp round. Seeing the boy scudding away at such a rapid pace, he very naturally concluded him to be the predator; and, shouting "Stop thief!" with all his might, made off after him, book in hand.

2 But the old gentleman was not the only person who raised the hue-and-cry. The Dodger and Master Bates, unwilling to attract public attention by running down the open street, had merely retired into the very first doorway round the corner. They no sooner heard the cry, and saw Oliver running, than, guessing exactly how the matter stood, they issued forth with great promptitude; and shouting "Stop thief!" too, joined in the pursuit like good citizens.

3 Although Oliver had been brought up by philosophers, he was not theoretically acquainted with the beautiful axiom that self-preservation is the first law of nature. If he had been, perhaps he would have been prepared for this. Not being prepared, however, it alarmed him the more; so away he went like the wind, with the old gentleman and the two boys roaring and shouting behind him.

4 "Stop thief! Stop thief!" There is a magic in the sound. The tradesman leaves his counter, and the carman his waggon; the butcher throws down his tray; the baker his basket; the milkman his pail; the errand-boy his parcels; the school-boy his marbles; the paviour his pickaxe; the child his battledore. Away they run, pell-mell, helter-skelter, slap-dash: tearing, yelling, screaming, knocking down the passengers as they turn the corners, rousing the dogs, and astonishing the fowls: and streets, squares, and courts, re-echo with the sound.

5 "Stop thief! Stop thief!" The cry is taken up by a hundred voices, and the crowd accumulate at every turning. Away they fly, splashing through the mud, and rattling along the pavements: up go the windows, out run the people, onward bear the mob, a whole audience desert Punch in the very thickest of the plot, and, joining the rushing throng, swell the shout, and lend fresh vigour to the cry, "Stop thief!"

Name _____   Oliver Twist 2

1.   Below is a brief summary of each of the five paragraphs in the text. Number
      them in the correct order. The first one is done for you.

Dodger and Bates were hiding in a doorway but when they saw the situation they ran after Oliver too, shouting "Stop Thief!" as if they were good citizens.	
More people joined in running through the muddy streets, the crowd getting bigger all the time.	
The old gentleman saw Oliver running away and mistakenly thought he was the one who had stolen his handkerchief. He shouted, "Stop thief!"	**1**
Oliver could not believe what was happening to him. He became so alarmed that he ran faster, with the old gentleman and the two boys shouting behind him.	
All the trades people left their work and ran after Oliver too, shouting, "Stop thief! Stop thief!"	

2.   Look up the meanings of the following, in a dictionary or thesaurus:

(**depredator**) _____

_____

(**promptitude**) _____

_____

(**hue and cry**) _____

_____

3. The language that Dickens used in Victorian times is different to the language we use today. The sentence at the start of paragraph 3 is particularly difficult:

"Although Oliver had been brought up by philosophers, he was not theoretically acquainted with the beautiful axiom that self-preservation is the first law of nature."

Dickens is saying that Oliver had been brought up by 'thinking' people but he had not been taught that 'self-preservation is the first law of nature'.
What do you think Dickens means by the phrase underlined?

_____

_____

_____

_____

4. In each phrase below, replace the word underlined with another which has the same or similar meaning and rewrite the phrase.

joined in the **pursuit**

_____

_____

retired into the first doorway

_____

_____

seeing the boy **scudding** away

_____

_____

the crowd **accumulated** at every turn

_____

_____

This unit addresses the Literacy Strategy:
Term 1 objective   1: to analyse features of a good opening and compare a number of story openings.
Term 2 objective   7: to compile a class anthology of favourite poems with commentaries which illuminate the choice.
Term 3 objective   6: to explore the challenge and appeal of older literature through; listening to older literature being read aloud; reading
                     accessible poems, stories and extracts; reading extracts from classic serials shown on television; discussing differences in
                     language used.

Name   The Lamplighter

The texts on these two pages are both entitled 'The Lamplighter'. One is a poem by the poet Robert Louis Stevenson. The other is the opening paragraphs from 'The Lamplighter', a little known novel by an author called Miss Cummings.

The Lamplighter
by Robert Louis Stevenson

My tea is nearly ready and the sun has left the sky;

It's time to take the window to see Leerie going by;

For every night at teatime and before you take your seat,

With lantern and with ladder he comes posting up the street.

Now Tom would be a driver and Maria go to sea,

And my papa's a banker and as rich as he can be;

But I, when I am stronger and can choose what I'm to do,

O Leerie, I'll go round at night and light the lamps with you!

For we are very lucky, with a lamp before the door,

And Leerie stops to light it as he lights so many more;

And O! before you hurry by with ladder and with light,

O Leerie, see a little child and nod to him tonight!

Extract from 'The Lamplighter' by Miss Cummings

It was growing dark in the city. Out in the open country it would be light for half an hour or more; but within the close streets where my story lead me it was already dusk. Upon the wooden door-step of a low-roofed, dark, and unwholesome-looking house, sat a little girl, who was gazing up the street with much earnestness. The house-door, which was open behind her, was close to the sidewalk; and the step on which she sat was so low that her little feet rested on the cold bricks. It was a chilly evening in November, and a light fall of snow, which had made everything look bright and clean in the pleasant open squares near which the fine houses of the city were built, had only served to render the narrow streets and dark lanes dirtier and more cheerless than ever;

for, mixed with the mud and filth which abound in those neighbourhoods where the poor are crowded together, the beautiful snow had lost all its purity.

A great many people were passing to and fro, bent on their various errands of duty or of pleasure; but no one noticed the little girl, for there was no one in the world who cared for her. She was scantily clad, in garments of the poorest description. Her hair was long and very thick; uncombed and unbecoming, if anything could be said to be unbecoming to a set of features which, to a casual observer, had not a single attraction, being thin and sharp, while her complexion was sallow, and her whole appearance unhealthy.

She had, to be sure, fine dark eyes; but so unnaturally large did they seem in contrast to her thin puny face, that they only increased the peculiarity of it, without enhancing its beauty. Had any one felt any interest in her (which nobody did), had she had a mother (which alas! she had not), those friendly and partial eyes would perhaps have found something in her to praise. As it was, however, the poor little thing was told, a dozen times a day, that she was the worst-looking child in the world; and, what was more, the worst behaved. No one loved her, and she loved no one; no one treated her kindly; no one tried to make her happy, or cared whether she were so. She was but eight years old, and all alone in the world.

There was one thing, and one only, which she found pleasure in. She loved to watch for the coming of the old man who lit the street-lamp in front of the house where she lived; to see the bright torch he carried flicker in the wind; and then, when he ran up the ladder, lit the lamp so quickly and easily, and made the whole place seem cheerful, one gleam of joy was shed on a little desolate heart, to which gladness was a stranger; and, though he had never seemed to see, and certainly had never spoken to her, she almost felt, as she watched for the old lamplighter, as if he were a friend.

Poem

1. Name the author of the poem 'The Lamplighter'.

    _____

2. What is the name given to the lamplighter?   _____

3. How many children are in the poem? Can you name all of them?

    _____

    _____

4. What is their father's profession?

    _____

Novel

5. Explain how you know it is early evening when the story begins?

    _____

    _____

6. Is the story set in the city or the country? Use words from the text to explain how you know this.

    _____

    _____

7. Describe the weather at the start of the story.

    _____

    _____

8. What did the little girl in the story love to do?

    _____

    _____

9. Write any particular words or phrases that indicate that the text is a very old one.

    _____

    _____

    _____

    _____

Poem

10.   How many rhyming couplets make up 'The Lamplighter' poem? _____

11.   What is Tom's ambition? _____

12.   Why does the lamplighter carry a ladder?

      _____

13.   **Extra Activity**
      Investigate other poems by the same author. Present your favourite in your
      neatest handwriting, and illustrate it with care. Give reasons for your choice of
      poem. Many more poems by Robert Louis Stevenson can be found in 'A Child's
      Garden of Verse'.

 **Novel**

14.   Which word in the fourth sentence gives you
      the first clue that the novel is set in North America? _____

15.   Write the word that is normally used in Britain meaning the same as the word
      that was your answer to the previous question. _____

16.   Write the sentence from the text that tells you the child was very poorly dressed.

      _____

      _____

17.   How old was the child? _____

18.   Write the phrase that tells you she had no family.

      _____

19.   Rewrite the story in your own
      words. Your version may not be so
      long, but it will sound up-to-date
      and include all the important
      details.

This unit addresses the Literacy Strategy:
Term 3 objective 12: to read and evaluate letters, e.g. from newspapers, magazines, intended to inform, protest, complain, persuade, considering
i) how they are set out, ii) how language is used, e.g. to gain attention, respect, manipulate.

YEAR	UNIT	Sheet
5	21	A

Name

Letters

  Letter 1

17 Brown Lane
Sullompton
Devon
DX13 0TN

The Editor
Tivertee Star
South St
Tivertee
Devon
DX14 7EX

14 April 2002

Dear Sir/Madam,

I am writing to your paper to express my disgust about the state of the pond in Viva Park. I walk past it most days, and have noticed, each day, that it is getting more dirty and untidy. There are newspapers and plastic bottles floating in the water making it look an unsightly mess. There is also a large amount of dog mess around the area. This is unpleasant for everybody, but it is especially dangerous for young children, who may get ill as a result of it.

I have heard that litter and dog droppings are a problem in many towns, and feel that someone should investigate how other councils are trying to solve the problem of untidy parks.

I know that council money has to be used for many purposes, but I do think that a few dog wardens in the park, making people collect their dog's mess, would make a difference. In my opinion, it is a shame to see so lovely a park in such a mess. I expect the council to give this matter their full and careful consideration.

I look forward to receiving your reply.

Yours faithfully,

J. Smith

Jill Smith

Letter 2

Carpet Time
106 Watley Street
Burtin
BR6 7UT

T.N. Khan
14 Arrow Way
Burtin
BR5 7UH

26 October 2002

Dear Mrs Khan,

Re: Axal carpet.

Further to your letter dated 18 October, I have given your complaint further consideration.

Although your new Axal carpet was advertised as stain resistant to everyday stains, I am sure you must appreciate that stain 'resistant' is not the same as stain 'proof.' Extensive tests have been carried out in our laboratories and the carpet performs well with normal day-to-day stains which are removed straight away with a damp cloth. The hour-long nose bleed that your husband was unfortunate enough to experience, and the pool of blood that collected on the carpet, could not really be termed an 'everyday stain'. Blood is a particularly difficult stain to remove, and needs prompt attention and I believe you stated, in your previous letter, that you were not able to attend to the stain for some hours.

In the circumstances, I regret that we cannot refund the cost of your carpet as you request, but as a token of our goodwill, I have enclosed a £10 voucher. Please do not hesitate to contact me if you wish to discuss this matter further.

Yours sincerely,

R.N.Passmore

Mr Ronald Passmore
Customer Information Services

Name _____   Letters

Both of these letters are **formal** letters.

1. For each letter, write a couple of sentences saying why the writer wrote the letter.

   Letter 1 _____

   _____

   _____

   Letter 2 _____

   _____

   _____

In a formal letter, a different type of language is used to the language in a more chatty informal letter. It is not the language we normally use when speaking to each other. Shortened words are not used, e.g. **won't** is written **will not**.

2. Here are some shortened words (contractions). Write them out in full:

   can't _____   **we've** _____

   you'll _____   **I'll** _____

   didn't _____   **it's** _____

   wouldn't _____

3. Look at letter 1. Change these formal phrases into more informal language. The first one is done for you.

   express my disgust _____ tell you that I'm very upset _____

   unsightly mess _____

   could investigate _____

   full and careful consideration _____

4. Now look at letter 2. Again, change the formal phrases into more informal language. The first one is done for you.

   further to your letter _____ thanks for your letter _____

   further consideration _____

   unfortunate enough to experience _____

   _____

   in the circumstances, I regret _____

   _____

These are all the beginnings or ends of informal letters:

14D White Tower
London
SE14 9PX
2.6.02

Hi Sarah,
It was great to see you the other day and catch up on all the gossip.

So thanks again for the great present.

    Love Sonia

See you on Sunday. Cheers mate,

Abdul

20A Landale Court
Sheffield
SH7 6RT

Dear Mum and Dad,
Great news....

5.   The layout of an informal letter is different to a formal one. Compare the formal letters with the beginning and ends of these informal letters.
Make a list of the differences that you notice.

_____

_____

_____

_____

_____

_____

_____

_____

6.   Choose one of the informal letters to complete on a separate piece of paper.
In an informal letter you can:

✓   sound natural and chatty
✓   still have proper sentences
✓   use more common words
✓   use shortened words like 'didn't'.

This unit addresses the Literacy Strategy:
Term 3 objective 13: to read other examples, e.g. newspaper comment, headlines, adverts, fliers. Compare writing which informs and persuades, considering, e.g. the deliberate use of ambiguity, half-truth, bias; how opinion can be disguised to seem like fact.
Term 3 objective 14: to select and evaluate a range of texts, in print or other media, for persuasiveness, clarity, quality of information.

YEAR	UNIT	Sheet		
5	22	A	Name	Flier, Press Release and Information Sheet

When new books are published, the publishers want as many people as possible to know about them. They produce information for bookshops, libraries and schools. They also inform newspapers, radio stations and television companies.

You are going to look at three different information sheets about a series of books called 'Reading for Literacy':

- **an advertising 'flier' (sheet B)**
- **an 'Advance Information' sheet (sheet C)**
- **a 'press release' (sheet D)**

The flier is an advertisement that is sent to schools.
The Advance Information (A.I.) sheet is sent to bookshops.
The press release is sent to newspapers and magazines.

1.   Which sheet would be used to try to persuade teachers to buy the books?
     (Your teacher has already bought one of the books because this sheet is part of it!)

     _____

2.   Which sheet tells retailers about the books before the books are published?

     _____

3.   Why do you think the publishers send out a press release?

     _____

     _____

     _____

4.   Where were the books published?

     _____

5.   How many books are in the set?

     _____

6.   In the press release, can you find a strange phrase that is used to show that lots of books have been sold?

     _____

7.   Try to find out what ISBN stands for.

     _____

The Literacy Strategy. Covered. ✓

A quarter of UK primaries use our photocopiables. Do you?

Reading for Literacy

NEW SERIES

A brand new series of six durable photocopiables designed to improve reading and comprehension skills across the primary age range. Includes a book for reading at Reception level.

- ✓ Complements our highly regarded and successful Writing for Literacy and Spelling for Literacy series.

- ✓ Follows the requirements of the National Literacy Strategy. Ideal for test practice.

- ✓ Contains a wealth of varied fiction and non-fiction units including scripts, advertising and persuasive texts, journalism, letters and poetry.

- ✓ Pages fold flat for easy photocopying.

- ✓ Each book in the series is available for £16.50 (5-7, which covers two years, costs £18.50). All six books are available for the special set price of £88*.

SPECIAL OFFER
Reading for Literacy complete set of 6 books **£88**

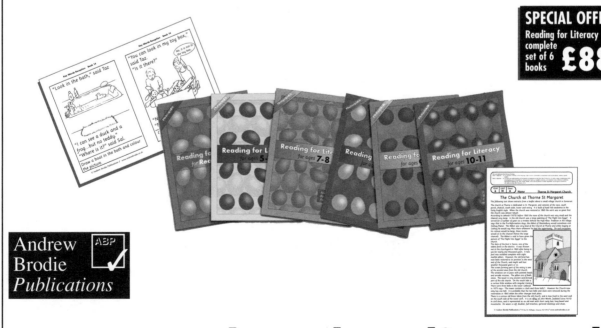

Andrew Brodie Publications

www.andrewbrodie.co.uk

© Andrew Brodie Publications ✓ www.acblack.com

ADVANCE INFORMATION

Title:	Reading for Literacy for ages 9-10
Publication Date:	December 2002 Product Format: Book, paperback
Editor:	Brodie, Andrew Keith
Authors:	Richardson, Judy; Wiltshire, Tess; Brodie, Andrew

ISBN: 1897737 85 8   Price: £16.50

Dimensions:	297mm high x 220mm wide
No of pages:	104 + cover
Subject:	Children's Educational, School and College Text
Availability:	IN PRINT FROM 14TH DECEMBER 2002

Description of subject matter:

Photocopiable resource book for teachers, providing a complete programme of reading activities. Designed to help teachers with the National Literacy Strategy.

Place of publication:	Wellington, Somerset, England
Readership Level:	Children, Primary
Publisher Name:	Andrew Brodie Publications
Publisher Address:	PO Box 23, Wellington, Somerset, TA21 8YX
Telephone:	01823 665493
Fax:	01823 665345
Email address:	andrew@andrewbrodie.co.uk
Website:	www.andrewbrodie.co.uk
Distributors:	Andrew Brodie Publications
	PO Box 23, Wellington, Somerset, TA21 8YX

Territorial Market Rights: Publisher holds world-wide rights.

Author Information:

All of the authors have extensive experience in primary and secondary education.

The Literacy Strategy. Covered. ✓

Reading for Literacy...

...a brand new range of photocopiables from Andrew Brodie publications.

Educational publisher Andrew Brodie Publications has announced its latest series of teachers' photocopiable literacy books. The series, Reading for Literacy, provides a brand new scheme designed to improve reading and comprehension skills across the primary age range. Written to complement the highly regarded and successful Writing for Literacy and Spelling for Literacy, Reading for Literacy also precisely follows the requirements of the National Literacy Strategy.

Each of the six books is split into units, each with its own reading material and related exercises to promote better reading and understanding. The series contains a wealth of varied fiction and non-fiction reading material to stimulate interest and the imagination. Areas covered include scripts, advertising and persuasive texts, journalism, letters and poetry.

Andrew Brodie Publications' Sales Manager, Clare Turner explains how teachers can also benefit from this series: "The books help to make teachers' lives easier by saving them hours of preparation time," said Turner. "Each book contains comprehensive notes and suggestions for teachers and this scheme is ideal to assist teachers in preparing their pupils for SATs tests, too."

The rugged books are designed to withstand constant use and each sheet is also conveniently hole-punched enabling it to be added to teachers' files alongside other notes. All the pages are also perforated, allowing them to fold flat for easy photocopying if kept in the book. Each book in the series is available for £16.50 (5-7, which covers two years, costs £18.50). The set of six books is also available to educational establishments at the special price of £88.

Somerset-based Andrew Brodie Publications has been selling books by the bucketload during 2002, having notched up sales of over 550,000 copies since the first title, Times Tables Today, was launched in 1992. The launch of Reading for Literacy follows a year in which the publisher has experienced remarkable success selling more books not only to chains and wholesalers but also direct to schools.

Reading for Literacy for Reception
1897737 61 0   £16.50

Reading for Literacy for ages 5-7
1897737 36 X   £18.50

Reading for Literacy for ages 7-8
1897737 41 6   £16.50

Reading for Literacy for ages 8-9
1897737 46 7   £16.50

Reading for Literacy for ages 9-10
1897737 51 3   £16.50

Reading for Literacy for ages 10-11
1897737 56 4   £16.50

This unit addresses the Literacy Strategy:
Term 3 objective 12: to read and evaluate letters, e.g. from newspapers, magazines, intended to inform, protest, complain, persuade, considering, i) how they are set out ii) how language is used, e.g. to gain attention, respect, manipulate.
Term 3 objective 15: from reading, to collect and investigate use of persuasive devices: e.g. words and phrases: e.g. 'surely', 'it wouldn't be very difficult...', persuasive definitions, e.g. 'no-one but a complete idiot...'., 'every right-thinking person would...', 'the truth is...', rhetorical questions ' are we expected to...?', 'where will future audiences come from', pandering, condescension, concession etc.; 'Naturally, it takes time for residents..', deliberate ambiguities, e.g. 'probably the best.. in the world', 'known to cure all', 'the professionals' choice'.

YEAR 5	UNIT 23	Sheet A	Name	Persuasive Text

27 Green Lane,
Clayhall,
Alverstone,
Devon

14th February 2003

The Editor
Tivertee Star
South St
Tivertee
Devon
DX14 7EX

14 April 2002

Dear Sir,

I noticed with horror, this evening in your newspaper, an article about the large housing estate that the Council are proposing to build near Green Lane. Do they realise the serious implications this will have? This part of town already has too many houses. Surely it wouldn't be very difficult to find an alternative site for these houses.

As a resident of Green Lane, I feel sure that I speak for many others who live in this neighbourhood. Naturally I don't expect the Council not to build any new houses in this area and I understand the Council's problems in finding somewhere suitable, but in my opinion Green Lane is not the place for such a large number of houses. I have conducted a survey of the area, and discovered that there is only one shop, no garages, no Youth Club, only one church and one school, all some walking distance away. These new houses would bring in far too many people for these facilities to cope with.
This is a lovely green part of town where people can enjoy the open spaces.

Perhaps the old brick factory at the other end of town would be a more suitable site. Please ask the Council to think again and save our town's green spaces.

Yours faithfully

Ian Bagshot

1.   Where does Mr Bagshot live?

_____

2.   Why do you think Mr Bagshot does not want the houses built?

_____

_____

3.   Persuasive devices are words and phrases used by the writer to make us believe or accept what he is writing.
      What words and phrases does Mr Bagshot use to try to persuade people?

      a._____

      b._____

      c._____

      d._____

      e._____

4.   What do the words 'I feel sure I speak for many others' tell us?

_____

_____

5.   The letter is divided into three paragraphs. Join the correct paragraph number to its description.

(**Paragraph 1**)   (**Offers a possible solution to the problem.**)

(**Paragraph 2**)   (**Introduces the purpose of the letter and describes the problem.**)

(**Paragraph 3**)   (**Gives details of the argument and tries to change the reader's opinion.**)

6.   Write a letter to the newspaper regarding an issue you feel strongly about.
      Use the paragraph model to plan your letter clearly.

PURCHASE PANTHER PERFORMANCE
FOR POWER AND PERFECTION.
CAN YOU CONTROL THE
POWER OF THE PANTHER?

The bike of the century

with its amazing new revolutionary braking system, the new PANTHER 4041 is probably the best in the world. This superb new bike will revolutionise the biking world. Tests have shown that the PANTHER is stronger and easier to handle with more manoeuvrability than most other bikes in its class.

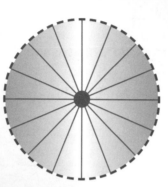

SPECIFICATION

- Frame Aluminium 4041 series
- Braking System Mega x system
- Gear System Suman 27 speed
- Tyres Gripfast 26 x 19.5"
- Colour Silver/Grey
- Sizes 43-53cm
- Price £499.95

GUARANTEED TO DELIGHT

GET DOWN TO YOUR LOCAL STOCKIST NOW BEFORE YOU ARE TOO LATE TO CAPTURE YOUR PANTHER.
IT'S A WILD BEAST OF A MACHINE!

1. What do you notice about the caption on the top of the advert?
   Read it aloud. What do you notice about the words?

   _____

2. Why do you think the advertisers have done this?

   _____

   _____

3. a. How many times does the word PANTHER appear in the advert? ☐

   b. Why do you think it appears so many times?

   _____

4. List all the words and phrases that are used to persuade us to buy the bike.

   a._____

   b._____

   c._____

   d._____

   e._____

   f._____

Name   Persuasive Text

5.   Why do the advertisers put 'probably the best in the world'?

_____

_____

6.   a.   Do you think the Panther is really stronger and easier to handle than all
            other bikes?

      _____

      _____

      b.   How do you know?

      _____

      _____

7.   Opinion is often disguised as facts by some advertisers. Sort these words and
      phrases into fact or opinion.

> **performance for power and perfection**   size 43-53cm   **new braking system**
>
> **Price £499.99**   **revolutionise the biking world**   **available in Silver/Grey**
>
> **probably the best in the world**   **bike of the century**   **Gripfast tyres**

FACT	OPINION

8.   a. Write your own factual advert for the new Panther bike, on a separate sheet.
      b. Which advert (yours or the advertiser's) would make you want to buy the
      bike? Why?

This unit addresses the Literacy Strategy:
Term 1 objective   23: to discuss the purpose of note-taking and how this influences the nature of notes made.
Term 2 objective   20: note making: to discuss what is meant by 'in your own words' and when it is appropriate to copy, quote and adapt.
Term 3 objective   16: note making: to fillet passages for relevant information and present ideas which are effectively grouped and linked.

YEAR	UNIT	Sheet
5	24	A

Name

The Great Fire of London

The Great Fire of London

1.   In the seventeenth century, most buildings in Britain were built of wood and thatch. Some churches were made of brick and stone, but most ordinary houses and shops were made of wood and various other materials, and had a thatched roof. Small fires often broke out in the towns and cities of Britain, and London was no exception. The Great Fire of 1666, however, was not a small fire. It caused massive destruction and changed the way London looked forever.

2.   In 1665, London was already a large city, bigger than any other city in Britain. The main area was within the city walls, that had been built over 2000 years before, by the Romans. There was only one bridge across the River Thames, and that was a wooden bridge known as London Bridge. This bridge had been built in the thirteenth century, and was lined with houses and shops. The timber-framed houses that ran along by the water front were crowded together, with barely enough room for carts to get along them. The river itself was often used for transporting goods from one part of the city to another.

3.   In 1665, London had suffered one of the worst outbreaks of plague that it had ever experienced. The Plague was an infectious disease that was spread by the fleas from rats. It caused the patient to have a high temperature and to vomit, and large pus-filled lumps appeared all over the body. Most patients died within a few weeks of getting the disease. Hundreds of people died in London, every week, from the Plague. When the fire broke out on 2nd September 1666, in a bakery in Pudding Lane, nobody thought that it was more than just another small fire.

4.   Pudding Lane was a dark, narrow, cobbled street. The bakery was owned by a family called Farynor, and the fire started in the middle of the night. Fortunately, Farynor and his family escaped, although it is said that the maid remained and became the first victim of the fire. There was a strong wind blowing from the north-east that night, and by morning already hundreds of houses had burnt down. By the evening, the wooden bridge was in danger, and the fire could be seen from some distance away. By the 3rd September, the whole of the river front right up to the Tower of London was ablaze. That night the city was as light as it was in the day time, because of the light from the fire. The King ordered that some houses should be pulled down in the path of the fire in the hope that if the fire had nothing to burn, then it would go out. The fire, however was spreading too fast, and thousands of buildings were on fire. People were trying to fight the fire by pulling the burning thatch off the houses, and squirting water from small pumps. The pumps, however, were too small, and with too little power, which made them ineffective.

5.   Tuesday, 4th September, was the worst day of the fire and Samuel Pepys, a famous man of those times who kept a diary, wrote that he had taken all his valuables and family out of London to keep them safe. He also said that he had buried his wine and cheese in his back garden! The fire had spread to outside the city walls. Inside the walls, over half the area was ablaze. Flames over 100m high could be seen leaping into the sky. All the shops, public buildings and some churches had been destroyed. The Lord Mayor of London was slow to decide what needed doing to stop the fire. King Charles the Second finally persuaded people that they needed to pull down, or blow up enough houses to make a gap large enough that the fire could not leap across. Chains of people passing buckets of water from hand to hand to douse the flames, were also organised.

6.   By Wednesday, the wind had dropped, and the fire slowed its pace. The buckets of water and the demolition of the buildings were at last taking effect. Amazingly, only eight people died in the Great Fire of London, but thousands were made homeless. People, who only a week ago, had been wealthy, now had nothing left. Many people had to live in huts or tents, with very few possessions, for a long time.

7.   London was rebuilt, but not with wood and thatch this time. Fine houses of brick and stone were erected, and the opportunity was taken to make wider streets with better drainage and pavements. It took many years to rebuild the centre of London  again, but when it was finished, it was once more a very grand city. Many people believe that the fire was a blessing, as it made London a healthier place to live.

Name _____

The Great Fire
of London

1. When was the Great Fire of London? _____

2. Where did the fire begin? _____

3. What other catastrophe had happened in 1665? _____
   _____

4. Identify the key ideas from each paragraph and make brief notes about them.

   1. _____
   _____

   2. _____
   _____

   3. _____
   _____

   4. _____
   _____

   5. _____
   _____

   6. _____
   _____

   7. _____
   _____

5. List the key words that tell you what London looked like before the Great Fire.
   _____
   _____

6. Now list the key words that tell you what London looked like after the Great Fire.
   _____
   _____

7. On the back of this sheet, use your key words to write some sentences of your own, comparing London before and after the Great Fire.

8. Scan the text, then highlight/underline any information that refers to 2nd September 1666.

9. Now use different colours to highlight/underline any information for 3rd, 4th and 5th September 1666.
    Use the information from the text that you have highlighted/underlined to write brief diary entries for those days.

2nd September 1666 _____

_____

3rd September 1666 _____

_____

4th September 1666 _____

_____

5th September 1666 _____

_____

Sometimes, for an answer, you are asked to **copy** the words or phrases from the text. You must **copy** the exact words from the text.

10. Copy the words or phrases in the text that tell you what Samuel Pepys did with his cheese and wine during the fire.

_____

_____

Sometimes you have to give an answer in your own words but you will need to show which part of the text backs up your answer. You will need to **quote** from the text, and the part which you quote needs to be in quotation marks. e.g. I think that the people of London must have been very scared during the great fire because, 'flames over 100m could be seen leaping into the sky' and this would have been very frightening.

11. What do you think it was like in the time of the Plague? Write your answer in your own words but **quote** from the text to back up your answer. Don't forget the quotation marks.

_____

_____

_____

_____

12. If you **adapt** a text, it means that you use the information in the text, but write it all in your own words, for a specific purpose. Write a few sentences, as if you are a reporter, reporting on how the new city of London looks many years after the fire.